Manuel Weltman

&

Raymond Lee
Best wishes

Pearl White

The Peerless Fearless Girl

Pearl White

THE PEERLESS FEARLESS GIRL

by
Manuel Weltman
and
Raymond Lee

South Brunswick and New York: A. S. Barnes and Company
London: Thomas Yoseloff Ltd

© 1969 by Manuel Weltman and Raymond Lee
Library of Congress Catalogue Card Number: 69-15769

A. S. Barnes and Co., Inc.
Cranbury, New Jersey 08512

Thomas Yoseloff Ltd
108 New Bond St.
London, W1Y OQX, England

SBN: 498 06860 9
Printed in the United States of America

To
John and Dorothy Hampton,
and their Silent Movie Theater,
where this book was born.

Contents

Acknowledgments

We express our thanks for the help supplied by the following people in the five years of research on this book.

Academy of Motion Picture Arts and Sciences, American Hospital (Paris, France), C. A. Auzello, J. Thorton Baston, Spencer Bennet, Mrs. Nellie Blackwell, Jacques Charles, The Library of Congress, Joe Cuny, Mrs. Mary Dass, Tom Dino, Mrs. G. W. Duvall, Mrs. G. E. Fender, Charles Ford, Earle Fox, Mrs. Eileen George, Mrs. Willard Greene, John Hampton, A. D. Harris (The Oklahoma Publishing Company), Mrs. Janet Harris, Mrs. Earl B. Hinken, Kenneth B. Holmes (Missouri Historical Society), Stuart Holmes, Mrs. Scena R. Howe, Lloyd Hughes, O. E. Jennings, Richard LaMarr, Robert Lee, Miss Jacqueline Lenoir, Russell P. MacFall, Leon Mathot, Mrs. Ethel McCurdy, Walter McGrail, Arther Miller, Mrs. Bertram Millhauser, Frank Moran, Newspaper editors (Both here and abroad), Wally Oettel, Mrs. Coralie Peiffer, Louis W. Reps, John T. Robyns, George Roussos, Miss Sharon Ryan, Mrs. George B. Seitz, Mrs. Ida Shatkin, Frank Leon Smith, Edward Snyder, Jim Stark (Green Ridge Local News), Her Majesty Queen Victoria Eugenia, Wallace Walthall, The Pearl White estate, Mrs. Marie Younger.

Pearl White

The Peerless Fearless Girl

Poor Pauline, I pity poor Pauline!
One night she's drifting out to sea,
Then they tie her to a tree,
I wonder what the end will be,
This suspense is awful!
Bing! Bang! Biff! They throw her off a cliff,
They dynamite her in a submarine.
In the lion's den she stands with fright,
Lion goes to take a bite—
Zip goes the film—Good night!
Poor Pauline.*

Prologue

In 1918 the Germans were making their last push to seize Paris. Big Bertha cannons bombarded the city of light, and bombs fell from the sky. Vicente Blasco Ibanez, famed Spanish novelist, whose *Blood and Sand* and *The Four Horsemen of the Apocalypse* became vehicles for Valentino, stumbled through the darkness hoping to find an air-raid shelter.

Following a line of people he descended into a cellar and sighed with relief.

Suddenly, there appeared on the screen the image of a flashing beautiful blond woman, defying death in a leap over the fire escape of a tall building.

He wiped the sweat and grime from his eyes. Where was he? What were all these people doing watching a shadow on a screen while hell raged above?

In his best French he asked a stout lady beside him what was happening.

"Monsieur," she said, "It's the last chapter of a Pearl White serial. We are most fortunate to see it, no matter what the Boche are trying to do."

Episode One:

The House of Unhappiness

Walking into the Pathé Studio at One Congress Street, Jersey City Heights, New Jersey, in 1914 to film *The Perils of Pauline,* Pearl White cut her long stride short, stopped, listened.

Clip, clip, clip . . .

She stared around letting the sunlight drifting through the glass roof outline people and objects.

Again that crazy sound. She looked toward the property room; it sounded like it was coming from there.

What was Pitch Revada up to now?

Pushing in the door, Pitch greeted her cheerily.

"Hi Pearl, how's the girl?"

And without batting an eye he continued clipping. What was he clipping? Again the semi-darkness blurred her vision.

Moving closer she saw something she couldn't believe even Pitch could be doing.

Clip, clip, clip . . .

Squatting before a large cage of scrambling rats, he held one in his gloved right hand while he clipped its teeth with shears he held in his left.

"Pitch, what in the hell are you doing?"

He smiled grabbing another kicking rat.

"Just a little manicurin'."

Pearl turned to the door and whirled back.

"Maybe you can do my molars after you finish with your friends."

After lunch the shooting shifted to the big water tank.

In the episode Pearl is trapped in an old mill which the villain is flooding. The waters rise higher and higher and Pearl struggles to keep from drowning and when it looks like she's a goner, Crane Wilbur, playing the hero, rescues her.

Climbing into the tank Pearl noticed Pitch in the background. Maybe she'd been a little blunt with him asking about those rats. He was a wonderful guy and well—today just wasn't her day, she guessed, thinking of the letter she'd received in the morning mail.

Cameraman Arthur Miller was ready to grind. Director Donald Mackenzie, was poised on one knee by the tank.

"OK, Pearl?"

"OK, Mac."

"Now, you know what to do. Soon as the water rises you look for a way out, then swim for it. Lots of horror on your face as you see there is no escape and the water rises and rises."

Stepping back and lifting his megaphone he shouted: "Lights! Camera! Action!"

Lights burning down, water pouring in, Pearl staring about horror struck, water rising higher and higher, Mackenzie shouting "More horror, Pearl, more horror!"

The water rising almost to her chin, she started to swim for it.

Mackenzie's voice echoed: "OK, Pitch, let them go!"

Pearl's thoughts whirled with the waters. What had Pitch to do with this scene? She half turned, getting a mouthful of water that almost choked the breath out of her. And then she saw the cage and Pitch lifting the latch and the rats leaping into the water swimming for their lives.

A wave of laughter rose above Pearl's fury. So it was funny to everybody, a real joke to pull on her! One of the rats jumped on her back.

"Mackenzie, you bastard," she screamed, "wait until I get out of here, I'll kick your head in!"

All the rats were scrambling on and around her; Pearl was now swimming for *her* life.

Broken glass shattered the watery confusion as Crane Wilbur crawled through a window and grabbed Pearl, rats and all, and hauled her to safety.

"Cut!" Yelled Mackenzie. "Great Pearl, just great; it was the best acting you ever did."

Slapping him across the face with a slimy hand she ran into the shadows.

Bumping into Louis Gasnier, presiding head of Pathé, she grabbed a rat still clinging to her shoulder and flung it at the elegant Frenchman.

"You dirty frog! I didn't sign a contract to play straight to a pack of rats!"

Gasnier's hand was on her arm. "But, ma cherie, when the fans see a beautiful woman so distressed it will be a sensation—it will make you an incomparable star."

Pearl tried to wring herself out.

"Pearl, let me make it up with you; tonight, a champagne dinner."

She knocked his hand away. "Take your paw off my tit!"

Donald Mackenzie, watching, sighed and said to the company: "That's it for today. See you tomorrow at eight."

Pearl streaked across the stage for her dressing room.

Mackenzie stared at Gasnier wiping himself off with a silk handkerchief.

He'd heard about this Frenchman annoying the extra girls. He'd heard a lot of things. As the Cooper-Hewitts dimmed and the shadows deepened he shook his head, picked up his script and walked slowly away from the tank where Pitch was still trying to gather up his frantic rats.

In her dressing room Pearl jerked off her blond wig, threw it on the floor and glared at her beautiful face in the mirror.

Was it her face? The wig sure made her over. Ever since she first wore it, playing a dual role for the Crystal film company, she had loved it.

But where was the real Pearl? Slowly she reached down, picked up the wig and dusted off some lint.

Opening the dressing table drawer she took a long pull at a half pint of Scotch. God, how she hated the stuff! Still, it steadied her nerves.

Why was she so depressed? After all it had ended long ago between her and Victor. She was starring in her own serial. Everybody predicted it would be a smash hit. And yet. . . . The past, it always turned up like a bad penny. Would she never forget those starvation days, her father, the struggle to be somebody?

There was a knock at the door. Again she could feel Gasnier's wrinkled hand on her breast.

That bastard!

Her face flushed again. If that was that frog she'd show him how she had handled those mashers when she was a trouper on the road.

Another knock. She felt the whiskey warm in her belly.

"Come in," she said gritting her teeth.

The door opened slowly, but before Pearl could throw the can of cold cream she was clutching in her hand, Pitch's voice stopped her.

"Don't throw it, Pearl! Wait a minute."

"Oh, it's you!"

"Gee Pearl, if I'd a known the rats were gonna upset you that much, honest I never would have let 'em go, no matter what Mackenzie ordered."

"Oh, its OK Pitch. To hell with the real rats; it's the human rats that get my dander up. Come on in. Sit down and have a drink."

Pearl took another shot as Pitch eased himself into a chair.

"I've never seen you so all of a heap." As he nipped from the bottle, "You faced more danger than those rats a dozen times, Pearl. Remember the scene where you were chasing the villains and you tried to jump from your car to theirs and slipped and fell in the street? All you did was get up and laugh though you almost busted your fanny."

Pearl tried to smile.

"How about that time the Chinese were dragging you through a secret panel in their café and you got stuck in the wall because it was too narrow and you were skinned from head to foot."

Pearl started to take her make-up off. Pitch studied her lovely face now slightly lined, the lips tight and her eyes with a faraway look in them.

"What is it, Pearl? Tell me."

She sighed and said: "It's a long story and not a very happy one."

He pulled his chair closer to the dressing table and lit himself a cigarette.

"Pearl we've been working on this serial for almost three months now and we've all gone through a lot of hell together and shared each other's problems, but we've also had a lot of yaks. You've been a reg'lar and stood up for us against the brass plenty a times. You know the whole damn crew would do anything for you."

Pitch handed her a towel.

As she rubbed off the greasepaint: "OK, Pitch, you asked for it. Better make it a crying towel."

For a moment she stared into the mirror and then half-whispered:

"Well, today I received the final papers for my divorce."

Pitch was bug-eyed. "Gee, Pearl, I didn't know you were even married."

Pearl lit a cigarette.

"Yeah, that's a story and a half. I had just turned eighteen and had left home against my father's wishes to go on the stage. When he saw me smoke a cigarette in a play he said I was headed for White Slavery, even tried to have a judge stop me. Well, my first work after that was with the Trousedale Stock Company. From the beginning I was fighting twenty-four hours a day for my virginity. One of the leading men, Victor Sutherland, a real handsome buck and a pretty decent guy, sort of shined up to me. Finally I propositioned him to go steady so the rest of the jokers would lay off.

"We toured around the Middle West playing one tank town after another for several months and then a day I'll never forget —October 12th 1907—dawned."

Pitch lit himself another cigarette.

"It was in Oklahoma City. We were playing *Amid the Hills Astray* at the People's Theatre. I was in the women's dressing room washing out some of my unmentionables when Minnie Remaley, the star of the show, came running in.

" 'Hey, Pearl,' she says to me, 'I just heard that the owner of this flea-trap is offering twenty-five bucks to any couple that'll get married on the stage after tonight's performance. Now look, I know that you and Vic are sweet on each other. So here's a way to get hitched and get paid for it.'

"I said, 'do you think he'd go for it?'

"She said, 'I already spoke to him. What do you think dearie?'

"Never been so damned nervous in my life out there in front of all those people. Pastor Harper married us and the place went wild. You'd think we were heroes of some kind. And like two crazy fools we blew the dough on a champagne breakfast."

For a moment Pearl's eyes misted. Suddenly she banged her fist on the table.

"Now, seven years later it's cost me five thousand dollars to get rid of him!"

"How come?"

"Well, we were just kids. Didn't know anything about life or love or anything. Something always happening. I was being fired all the time because . . . let's face it, Pitch, I'm a lousy actress.

"He wanted to become a Broadway star. We had to live with my father for a while. Victor couldn't find any kind of work. Pop called him a lazy bum. It was always . . ."

Pearl stopped in the middle of her sentence, her big brown eyes dilating.

As Pitch started to speak she put her finger to her lips and whispered: "Don't you hear what I hear?"

"I don't hear nuttin."

"Listen!"

A soft moan.

"I sure hear it now, Pearl."

"It's him again, Pitch, every Friday night like clockwork in that next dressing room."

Pearl's eyes gleamed; the trace of a snarl curled around her lips as she stood up and motioned Pitch to bring a chair to the opposite wall, cautioning him to be careful and not make any noise.

Pitch helped her on to the chair. At the top of the ceiling the partition was shy a foot so you could look over. Pearl leaned forward slowly inching her head up and looked over. A grin a yard wide crossed her face.

Looking down she whispered: "They're completely nude! Quick, dip those towels in the ice water cooler."

"Pearl, what you gonna do?"

"Cool off a volcano."

Pitch dragged the dripping towels from the cooler, handing them to Pearl who lifted them up as Pitch held tightly to the chair.

Suddenly she flung them over the partition. A moment of silence.

Screams and shouts!

Pearl and Pitch running out of the dressing room, across the darkened stage, into the night. . . .

TO BE CONTINUED

THE PERILS OF PAULINE

To Our Patrons:

It has been our object to put on at this theatre such photoplays as will be educational, interesting or amusing and which would not in any way offend anyone who might attend our performances. We would ask you to come to see the "PERILS OF PAULINE." We can recommend it as a serial intensely interesting and highly thrilling. "THE PERILS OF PAULINE" is a clean photoplay from beginning to end. You can bring the children and know that they will see only that which is beneficial to them. There are many thrills, many spectacular accidents and many dramatic situations in "THE PERILS OF PAULIN" which will keep your interest at fever heat through the whole episode. Some spectacular accident occurs in every episode; something which will startle you and something which you would imagine would be almost impossible for human beings to enact and survive. We would be very much pleased indeed to have you attend the showing of "THE PERILS OF PAULINE."

Paul Panzer, Frank Carlyle, and Donald Mackenzie, who played the role of a phony pirate in two episodes, pose in this old ad for one of America's most famous films.

Crane Wilbur helps our heroine out of her wrecked automobile.

Villains (*real* firemen don't wear earrings!) are dragging Pearl out of her house. Hero Crane Wilbur is unable to help her—for now.

Heroines descending staircases are traditional bits of cinema dramatics.

That must be the villain who's romancing Pearl. In those days, heros didn't have mustaches.

Crane Wilbur seems anxious to get off the phone; and with lovely Pearl
White waiting patiently for him, we can't say that we blame him.

Pearl in a rendezvous with Paul Panzer.

Pearl attends a ball, but monocled Paul Panzer seems more interested in the camera than the girl.

Paul and Pearl seem terrified of Donald Mackenzie (the director and the villain), and considering his terrifying appearance, they have good reason.

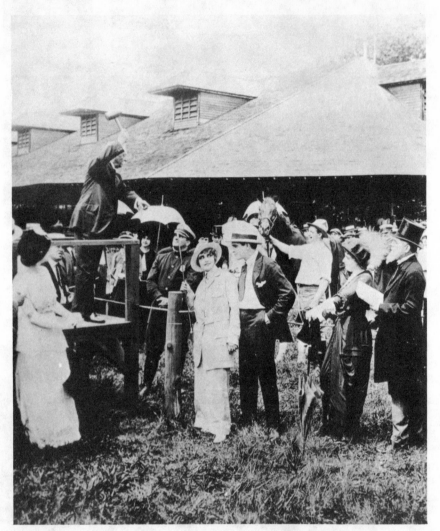

Pearl attends an auction with Crane Wilbur.

Three of *The Perils of Pauline's* principals: (Left to right) Pearl White, Crane Wilbur, Paul Panzer.

In this scene, Pearl gets involved with the army.

Donald Mackenzie as he appeared in 1914 (photo by Tom Dino) . . . and as he looked playing the pirate role in *Perils of Pauline*.

Villainous figures seem once again to be spiriting Pearl away.

Pearl and friends enjoy dinner in a Chinese restaurant.

Crane Wilbur on a raft, sailing toward Pearl?

Pearl aboard ship, with Paul Panzer.

A domestic scene? Left to right: Paul Panzer, Donald Mackenzie as the pirate, and Pearl, of course.

The side entrance to Pathé studios was used as a set.

Dr. Pepper float in 1968 Tournament of Roses Parade featured a *Perils of Pauline* theme. (Courtesy Dr. Pepper)

This photo, from Frank Carlyle's collection, features Frank along with Pearl and Paul . . . and pirate Donald.

We can't tell from this picture, but guess who's been tied to the tracks?

Episode Two:

Hurled into Space

"How do you feel in the balloon, Pearl?" Mackenzie asked his suspended star, as the morning sun haloed her head.

"Fine as long as this damn basket doesn't go up any further than the fifty feet you said it would."

"Don't worry, besides the four actors holding on to the safety lines, we have it attached to a fifty-foot cable wedged between those rocks over there with an anchor."

The director turned to Paul Panzer, the villain.

"All right, Paul, as you remember you're Pauline's secretary and next in line to her inheritance, and to get rid of her in this scene you pretend to take her picture in the balloon. Just as you snap the photo, your hired henchman on a supposedly runaway horse gallops into the crowd and knocks down the men holding the lines and the balloon soars out of camera range."

Mackenzie walked over to Arthur Miller, taking a final look through his lens at the long shot. Pitch handed the director his megaphone.

"Places everyone!" Mackenzie shouted. "Action! . . . Camera!"

The carnival crowd started to mill along the midway. Panzer and Pearl went into their pantomime. The balloon slowly rose.

Mackenzie was motioning the hired henchmen into the scene. Suddenly there was a crunching sound. The anchor had yanked free!

The four men struggled to hold the lines dragging across the ground!

A gust of wind sucked the balloon up, jerking one of the men twenty-five feet into the air.

Mackenzie was screaming: "Let go Sam, let go!"

Sam let go.

A woman in the stunned mob fainted.

35

A big black Packard screeched to a halt in the midway, Louis Gasnier leaped out: "Mon Dieu! Pearl my beautiful star where are you going?"

Mackenzie rushed up to him. "Louie, a gust of wind pulled the anchor free!"

Gasnier shouted: "Get in those cars and follow that balloon! Mackenzie come with me!"

As the two men jumped into the car, Gasnier turned and yelled at the hired henchman: "Cuny, you go on horseback!"

People and cars and one horse scattered like a stepped-on centipede.

The balloon was now at 4,000 feet, Pearl watched tight-lipped as the Palisades, between Fort Lee and Coytesville, became smaller and smaller and smaller.

The basket was being rocked back and forth by the buffeting winds. Thunderheads were darkening the eastern sky. Pearl muttered, "How in the hell am I going to get out of this?"

"Is it alright for me to come up now, Miss White?"

Pearl almost fell overboard from shock. Was she hearing things? Maybe her stepmother was right and the devil would get her after all.

Slowly the canvas on the bottom of the gondola rose. Pearl shrank back. It rose higher and higher. Her hand reached for a sand bag, trying to loosen it to slam it on whatever was rising. But catching sight of a man's bald head, Pearl stayed her clutching hand.

"I'm Leo Stevens, Miss White, the owner of this balloon."

"But what are you doing here?"

The little man stretched and smiled.

"Well, balloons are funny things—like people. Never know what they may do. I came along just in case anything went wrong."

Red-faced Pearl pointed, "Look down, buster, and you'll see plenty wrong."

Stevens looked down. "Not much to see now. A storm's really brewing.

"Well, Miss White, things aren't as bad as they seem. We're gonna have to ride this out."

"Mr. Stevens, I've ridden everything from the tops of freight cars to rafts on the high seas, but this isn't in my line. Isn't there something you can do?"

"Here chew on this piece of gum. It will keep your ears and nose from bleeding, because some times it happens up this far."

Pearl chewed. Stevens chewed. The balloon was almost chewed up by the winds.

There was a flash of lightning, a roll of thunder. And two small figures thrown together, dropped to the bottom of the wicker basket, as the rain pelted down like pebbles.

Pearl grabbed Stevens by the shoulders. "You really think we can weather this?"

Stevens smiled. "I been in the balloon business for half my life, Miss White, and I've seen these gassers take everything mother nature threw at 'em. I'm going to pull the ripping cord and let some gas out to take a sighting on where we may land."

The balloon began to descend.

Pearl and Stevens leaned over the basket, staring into the swirling mists, searching for a piece of terra firma.

"My God, Mr. Stevens, we're headed straight into that river!"

Stevens pulled more cords, rocking the balloon, acting like a magician emptying his bag of tricks.

Slowly the balloon hovered above the river, but just when it seemed it would flop in the water it rose swiftly.

The storm dissipated as suddenly as it had struck and long lanes of sunlight pointed out what resembled a square building in the middle of a plain.

"We'll try to set her down there, Miss White. Hold on."

Pearl, one hand on the basket and the other on her tummy, watched dizzily as the waiting ground came up closer and closer and closer.

Leo shouted: "Hold tight, Miss White, we'll bounce a couple times when we land."

And bounce they did. Pearl was almost thrown out, but Stevens, grabbing one of her legs, hauled her back; the bag sagged around them like a broken umbrella.

Three men in uniform carrying sawed-off shot guns rushed the basket.

"Get out and with your hands up!"

Pearl and Stevens tried to smile. "Gentlemen, there must be some mistake."

The tallest of the three stepped up. "Lady, there's no mistake. This is the Philadelphia State Penitentiary!

"You're in the prisoner's exercise yard."

Pearl stiffened. "Gentlemen, take us to your warden."

"Mr. Gasnier, Miss White calling from Philadelphia."

Gasnier grabbed the receiver wildly.

"Where are you? . . . What? . . . What are you doing there? . . . Are you alright? . . . Oh, thank God! . . . I'll send Joe Cuny to pick you up. Do you need anything, *ma cherie*?" . . . Gasnier smiled. "I'll send you a bottle of the best."

Whirling to his secretary, Gasnier barked out orders: "Get Cuny out to the Philadelphia State Penitentiary! Get William Randolph Hearst on the phone! And get me a brandy!"

Ten minutes later the phone rang.

"Mr. Hearst, I have some sensational news. Today on location in New Jersey while shooting a balloon sequence, Pearl White was hurled into space. She drifted for hours and just now landed. . . . Of course it will be an exclusive. She should be in my office in two hours for an interview."

Gasnier lit a cigarette.

"Oh, by the way, Mr. Hearst, how is the Pauline serialization contest doing in your papers? . . . Fine. . . . Already you've given away $10,000? . . . Wonderful. Well after reading the serial in your papers they're sure lining up at the box office. It was a tremendous idea to tie these two together, Mr. Hearst. You are to be congratulated. . . . Thank you, sir. Goodbye."

Gasnier leaped in the air. "This will make us another million!"

"Joe, you old bastard, am I happy to see you. Where's the bottle? . . . Boy! Did I need that."

Cuny gunned the big black Packard up to sixty as Pearl took a second swig.

"How do you feel, Pearl?"

"How would you feel being dragged up to 4,000 feet by a bag?"

"I've been dragged by many a bag, but not over four feet. But seriously, you OK?"

"Just a little air-sick, and a few bruises. I sure owe my life to that Leo Stevens. I hope he can get his balloon out of that stinking prison without damaging it any more."

Pearl lit a cigarette. I suppose that Gasnier's got every newspaper man in New York City waiting for me in his office."

"You can say that again."

"Joe, stop the car."

"You are sick!"

Pearl started to rip her clothes.

"Pearl, what in God's name are you doing?"

"Getting ready for my interview."

Pearl opened the door, reached down and grabbing a handful

of mud, spread it all over her dress, face and arms.

"You sure you didn't get a bump on the head?"

Pearl smiled, "You'll see. Put some horses on this wagon and let's roll!"

Gasnier stumbled back as Pearl stumbled into his crowded office.

"Mon Dieu! You *are* injured!"

Pearl threw her hand to her head in the best pantomime of the period.

"No, Louis, just a few bruises."

Pearl reeled.

Three chairs were pushed forward. Pearl refused them, leaning against the producer's desk looking as if she'd been netted from a swamp.

"Are you able to talk, *ma cherie*?"

Pearl's big eyes flashed at the sea of faces.

"How about a glass of water?"

Gasnier's secretary offered her one. Pearl frowned. Gasnier pressed it to her lips. She gulped it, almost choking.

Gasnier took her hand.

"Now, my incomparable star, are you ready to tell your story?"

Sighing deeply, brushing a chunk of mud off her cheek, looking slyly at Joe Cuny at the back of the room, she began.

. . . "And then as I thought all was lost, and I had made my peace with my Maker, Mr. Stevens spotted the New Lots waterworks, and said, 'this is were we must land, we're almost out of gas.'

"And land we did. The basket turned over, and I was hurled to the ground.

"The huge bag smothered all around me like a shroud. Almost unconscious I faintly heard shouts and screams, many hands clawing at the bag.

"When I felt I was breathing my last, suddenly the silk was pulled away and fresh air flooded over me.

"Someone called my name, many hands picking me up, tearing my clothes, shouting, 'It's Pearl White; it's Pearl White the movie star.'

"I thought they would shred me to pieces. And then Leo Stevens out of nowhere was directing the police on horseback to my rescue."

The reporters fired questions from all parts of the room.

Gasnier lifted his hands. "Gentlemen, Miss White has been through a terrible ordeal, she must rest. I will have her full statement sent to you by special messenger. Thank you gentleman, thank you for coming."

Motioning everyone out of his office, alone with Pearl, he stared at her in astonishment.

"Pearl, what's with this waterworks story? You called me from a prison."

Pearl sidled up to him, putting her arm around his shoulder.

"We did land in the prison, but the warden swore us to secrecy. He said for security reasons."

Gasnier warmed up to Pearl.

"This publicity will bring you millions of new fans. You will become a living legend."

Then stepping back from her, he continued:

"Truth has many faces, *ma cherie*. Never lose sight of your own."

A bewildered Pearl slowly walked out of his office.

TO BE CONTINUED

BEHID THE SCENES

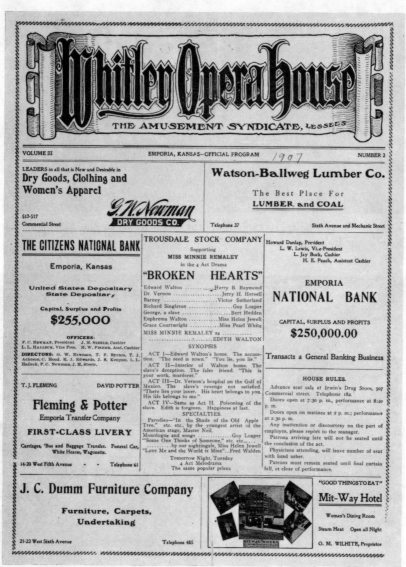

An ad from the period when Pearl was with the Trousdale Stock Company (1907). Note Victor Sutherland, Pearl's first husband, is in the cast.

Director George Seitz is explaining the next scene to the cast. Note Joe Cuny in the light cap.

Pathé cameraman Arthur Miller; he did the work for *Perils of Pauline*.

Pearl in a Fox Film publicity photo, for her 1920 motion picture, *The White Moll.*

On location at North Scituate, Mass.
The House of Hate
Front row, reading from left to right: Antonio Moreno. Seated: Pearl White, Helene Chadwick, Mrs. Arthur Miller, Mrs. Fred Seitz (George's mother.) Kneeling: Floyd Buckley. Standing: Frank Redman Jr. (Known as Bud), 2nd cameraman, Bill Burt, Harry (Deedee) Hardy, George Seitz, Arthur Miller, Morgan Jones, Charles (Pitch) Revada.

The Black Secret
Company on Pearl White's estate, Bayside Long Island.
Top: Bill Burt (Seitz assistant). Next left: Walter McGrail, Wallace
(Wally) McCutcheon (Pearl White's husband). Next left: George Seitz,
Pearl White, Mrs. Frank Leon Smith, Frank Leon Smith.

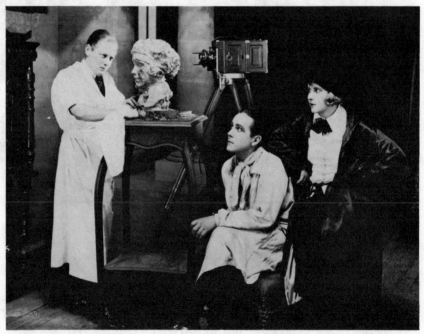

Robert Lee and Pearl watch her head being sculpted for *Perils of Paris.* . . .

Here Edward Jose joins the group.

Pearl and Edward Jose are waiting for the Paris sun to come out.

Pearl discusses script for *Perils of Paris* with Edward Jose (left) and leading man Robert Lee (right).

Pearl and cast and crew on location with *The Tiger's Cub*. Fox Films, 1920.

With George Seitz directing, Antonio Moreno is being held up, in *House of Hate*.

Horse play on set. (George Seitz is seen holding the script.)

Inside Pathé Studios as Pearl lets the villain have it.

Seitz directs this difficult scene . . . difficult for Pearl at any rate.

House of Hate: Louis Gasnier is at right. Seitz is the director, with stars
Antonio Moreno and Joe Cuny.

Episode Three:

The Baited Trap

Speeding along the Hudson River in her yellow Stutz Bearcat bound for Pathé Studios, the grey morning sky reflected the gloom that shadowed her face and drew tiny lines around her eyes. Suddenly Pearl pulled off her tam and let the wind whip through her dark brown hair.

Today was the last shooting on *Perils*. Today was the end of what had been the beginning—the years she had waited to become a movie star.

Today the future lay like a shining dollar in the palm of her hand.

Heads or tails?

Reaching in her purse for a cigarette a man's gold cufflink, on the seat, rolled against her hand.

Again she was in the Clover Club, again the horn player was making eyes at her, again she was asking the waiter to have the gentleman over for a drink.

So she went to his apartment and had a helluva lot of fun. He was a real sweet guy. In the morning she'd fixed bacon and eggs and he'd grabbed her hand and said he loved her. He didn't even know her name.

Of course he hadn't recognized her without her blond wig.

Was the wig only for make-believe? Was everything in her life to be make-believe? Written by Charles Goddard, directed by Donald Mackenzie, produced by Louis Gasnier . . . ?

Heading for an embankment Pearl braked the Stutz to a screeching halt.

Seconds later, appearing out of nowhere, was a police officer with pad in hand.

"Miss White, you could have killed yourself, you were hitting eighty."

"Oh, officer O'Toole! It's you again."

"Miss White this is the fourth time this month I've stopped you and I've never given you a ticket."

Pearl flashed him a coy smile.

"I know you must do your duty, officer, I won't make any excuses, but. . . ."

"But what?"

"Well, today is the last work on *Perils of Pauline,* and I guess my thoughts were just not on my driving."

Handing her the ticket, he said: "Please be careful, Miss White. For a second violation, the judge might even fine you two dollars!"

Mackenzie picked up his megaphone: "Well, this is the last shot folks, so let's make it great."

The bank of Cooper-Hewitt tubes were shedding their blue lights over the yacht as Crane Wilbur and Paul Panzer fought their last battle while Pearl stood in terror against the rail.

She threw herself back as Wilbur smashed Panzer in the jaw and he toppled over board.

Both stared down in horror as he sank into the propeller wash.

Mackenzie giving directions: "Pearl, bury your head in Crane's chest. . . .

"Crane put your arms around her . . . lift her chin up gently . . . That's it . . . Now kiss her."

Turning to the cameraman, "Arthur, start to iris out . . . Hold that kiss a little longer, OK, iris out. Cut! . . . That's it!"

As the lights began to go out, bedlam took over the set. An assistant jumped up on a chair; lifting his hands, he shouted everyone down: "Hold it folks, hold it everybody! Mr. Gasnier wants to speak to you."

Panzer climbed out of the tank.

"If anybody would like to know, I almost drowned on that last shot."

A grip hushed him as Gasnier stepped up on a platform.

"Ladies and gentlemen, this is an historic occasion. The last moment of a serial I know will one day go down as the greatest of all time . . . And a star-maker as well, thanks to our beautiful and fearless Pearl White."

All hands applauded.

"A bow to our fine actors, Crane Wilbur and Paul Panzer, and the supporting cast."

More applause.

"And what would we have done without director Mackenzie and cameraman Miller?"

Applause again.

"And all the rest of the crew who in the smallest way helped complete this great production."

Some one shouted from the crowd, "How about a hand for our producer, Mr. Gasnier?" The applause was a little less than enthusiastic. Gasnier smiled wryly.

"And now, ladies and gentlemen, tonight I will be your host at Reisenweber's in the Paradise room on the third floor."

There were waves of applause.

About to step down he added, "And Pearl, Paul and Crane, before I forget, we have a conference about our next serial in my office at ten tomorrow."

"How's Prince George the Loud?" Pearl quipped as she saw writer George B. Seitz sauntering down the hall towards Gasnier's office.

"I have a beastly hangover from last night's bash!" He replied in a Boston accent.

Wearing a tweed raglan overcoat, a blue suit, a yellow tie, yellow gloves, and derby hat, and swinging a knobby bamboo cane, he lived up to the odd nickname Pearl had given him.

"Have you ever been in a more fascinating place than Reisenweber's?" Pearl asked.

Seitz fanned himself with his derby. "I didn't get to see it all, were there really four floors?"

"Yes, and I ended up in the Hawaiian room, where I almost shook my hips out of joint trying to do the hula."

Seitz beat a tattoo on the floor with his cane. "It took my wife and me two hours to extract ourselves from some—dentist's banquet we stumbled into."

About to enter Gasnier's office, a jumble of loud, shouting voices stopped Pearl and Seitz. They waited listening.

"I don't give a damn, Louie. I want a sizeable raise or you'll get somebody else to play opposite Pearl. Besides I have an offer from Lubin."

Pearl grinned. "That's my boy Crane."

"Louis, I know *Perils* is making money hand over fist and I agree with Crane—all the principles should have a fair raise."

Seitz grinned. "And that is the notable villain Mr. Panzer

trying to act like a gentleman with a man he considers is not a gentleman."

The voices were jumbling again.

"Gentlemen, please, may I say something?"

Pearl croaked like a frog.

"Despite what you may have heard all the box-office returns are not in on *Perils*. We have high hopes but Pathé was not built on surmise.

"Facts, gentlemen, facts. I agree you should have a raise—but only half of what you ask."

Another outburst shook the walls.

Suddenly, Crane Wilbur yanked open the door and almost ran Pearl and Seitz down as he dashed out. Pearl and Seitz dusted themselves off only to be knocked off balance a second time by Panzer, who stopped to deliever an exit line.

"Louie, you'll be the death of Pathé yet with your conniving ways."

Pearl and Seitz exchanged puzzled looks. Then gently she tapped on the open door. There was a moment of silence as the wind whistled down the hall.

Gasnier's soft entrée brought them into his office.

"Well, how is my lovely star this morning?"

Pearl forced a smile. "Oh, fine Louie. Certainly a wonderful party last night."

"And you George, have a good time?"

"Mary and I really enjoyed it."

Pearl and Seitz sat down and waited as Gasnier kept smiling.

"George, your serial manuscript, *The Exploits of Elaine,* is tremendous; it will make us another million. And that villain you call "The Clutching Hand," he'll steal the picture."

Pear asked slyly, " 'The Clutching Hand?' Who's he?"

Seitz grinning. "Well, he's the man who has murdered your father and who you are trying to bring to justice with the aid of a scientific detective named Craig Kennedy."

Gasnier grinned. "And I've got a terrific actor, Sheldon Lewis, to play this monster. He'll scare the hell out of every serial fan in the world."

Pearl eased forward in her chair.

"Then Paul isn't going to be with us?"

"No, my dear, neither Paul nor Crane. I don't tolerate betrayal. You see, already I have signed their replacements."

Pearl and Seitz's faces went blank.

"But I want to reassure you, Pearl, there will be no quarrel between us.

"You are my star. I'll make you queen of the serials. And you will get a very nice raise."

Pearl, trying to act coy, failed.

"And George, I want you besides writer to be co-director with me. Mackenzie is scheduled for one of our features."

Gasnier rose.

"And now shall we leave the dull business of contracts to my lawyers?

"Come, I'll take you both to lunch."

TO BE CONTINUED

THE EXPLOITS OF ELAINE, NEW EXPLOITS OF ELAINE, ROMANCE OF ELAINE

This scene is from *The Romance of Elaine*. In this episode, "The Wireless Detective," hero Creighton Hale, is called upon to save Pearl from a watery grave.

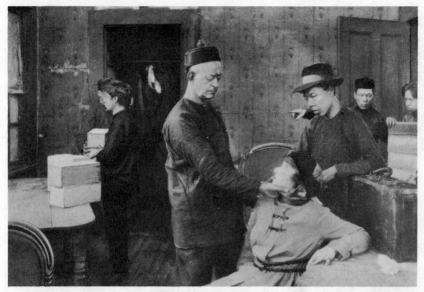

In *The New Exploits of Elaine,* Pearl ran into sinister Orientals in "The Opium Smugglers" episode. This scene, and the ones that follow, are stills from that chapter in Pearl's eventful on-screen life.

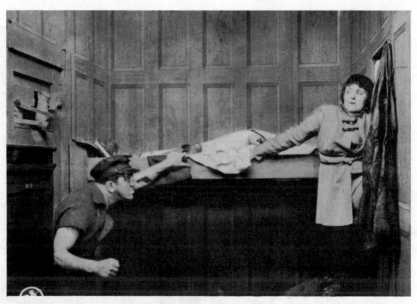

An encounter with a sailor.

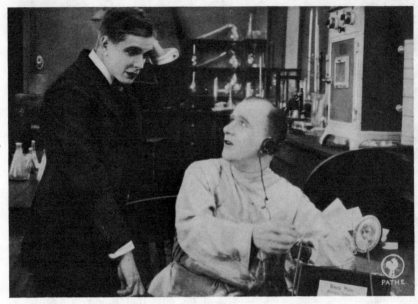

Creighton Hale tries to send a message.

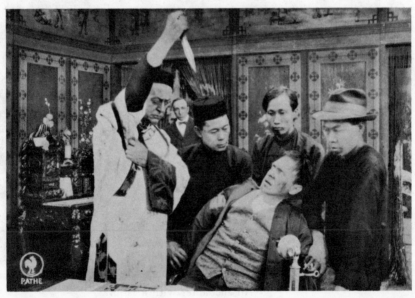

Is death to follow? Or is this just a speedy way of eliciting information. . . .

On the edge of disaster.

Escaping the villain's clutches.

With all those guns drawn, the villain hasn't a chance. (Creighton Hale looks on, at right.) This and the following scenes are from Episode 7 of *The Exploits of Elaine,* which was called "The Double Trap."

"Do you know how to shoot one of these?" the gentleman might have asked.

These uglies are giving Pearl a start. Well, you'd be scared too if you came up against these creeps.

Pearl looks innocent, Creighton Hale looks—well—clownish. But that man in the mask is certainly up to no good.

Episode Four:

She Clutching Hand

"The Clutching Hand! The Clutching Hand! The Clutching Hand!"

Two boys shouted after a tall dark man walking through the lobby of the Gold theatre in Chicago. He stopped and stared back.

People rushed up both aisles; a woman now took up the scream: "Call the police! Catch the Clutching Hand before he kills somebody! Call the police!"

The tall dark man made a quick exit with the crowd surging after him, as the manager of the theatre, Abe Gold, hurried out of his office and watched in amazement as his theatre was emptied of patrons watching the ninth episode of his biggest hit, *The Exploits of Elaine,* starring Pearl White and Sheldon Lewis as "The Clutching Hand."

Lewis scanned the street for a taxi—none in sight. A policeman—none in sight. Rushing into the corner drugstore he asked for a telephone.

As he dialed for the police the crowd gathered outside shouting: "Catch the Clutching Hand!"

The druggist stared at the man at the phone. He *was* the Clutching Hand.

He demanded Lewis leave immediately before the mob wrecked his pharmacy.

As the crowd pressed against the windows and the two boys pointed and jeered at him Lewis wondered why he had ever stopped in to see himself on the screen.

A policeman plowed through the milling throng and grabbed Lewis by the shoulders. Recognizing him he grinned: "You *are* the Clutching Hand!"

Sheldon nodded and added: "Get me out of here before they tear me limb from limb."

With the policeman running two hundred and fifty pounds of interference Sheldon Lewis followed the law through the raging mob, into the street and down an alley that led to the back of the theatre.

"You'll be safe here. I'm sure Abe Gold can get you transportation to your hotel."

"Officer, my deep thanks. But I'm catching the first train back to New Jersey."

The officer smiled: "Before I leave you Mr. Lewis, would you do me one favor?"

"Sure, you name it."

"Would you give me your autograph for my little girl?" The officer winked, "She hates the Clutching Hand too."

Lewis relaxing a bit reached into his pocket, pulled out one of his Pathé business cards, and quickly signed his name.

The two men waved goodbye and Lewis knocked on the back door.

No answer. He knocked again. He pounded. Only echoes down the alley.

And then slowly the voices of the mob again. Lewis kicked on the door which suddenly opened. He ran through, into the theatre, almost knocking down Abe Gold, who quickly locked and bolted the door.

In his office Gold handed Lewis a shot of Scotch.

"It always helps me over a crisis."

Lewis collapsed into a big leather chair.

"It's incredible, Mr. Gold. I can't believe it—that the public could hate me so."

Gold smiled.

"You are a great actor, Mr. Lewis. It's a wonderful tribute. In fact the fans are now calling *The Exploits of Elaine* "The Clutching Hand.""

"I wrote Mr. Gasnier about it suggesting he change the title."

"Well, Mr. Gold, you've been terrific, practically saved my life."

Both men laughed.

"For which I would like a small favor."

"Anything."

Mr. Gold sipped his scotch.

"The second show will soon end and I want to really surprise the audience—give them a rare moment to remember. A Gold-en moment, shall we say."

Lewis got the pun and smirked.

"Well, anything I can do——"

"I will appear before the audience and announce that never before in any theatre in America has The Clutching Hand appeared in person. But for Abe Gold he has consented to show himself."

Lewis leaped to his feet.

"Man, you must be mad! After what they've tried to do already——"

Mr. Gold sipped again and smiled.

"Mr. Lewis, I realize your anxiety. But would I let such a valuable property as The Clutching Hand be destroyed? I am a businessman. In the last weeks you have brought me my biggest business, no slight to lovely Miss Pearl White. I will have protection at every aisle and every exit and if a shall we say, calamity arises, I guarantee, and Abe Gold's word is gilt-edged, your safety regardless of the cost."

As Gold reached for the telephone, Lewis poured himself another Scotch, and true to his tradition as an actor toasted his destiny.

As the strains of the pipe organ faded away and the audience rustle began like a cat unravelling a ball of yarn, Abe Gold called for the house lights to be lowered, a spot beamed on the curtain, and through its center he bulged.

"Ladies and gentlemen, please hold your seats." A few belly-laughs.

"I mean, sit down." He waited as they sat down.

"You know Abe Gold has always brought you the best in movie and vaudeville entertainment." A confetti of applause. "But this afternoon I bring you a moment for all to remember." Murmurs; someone shouted: "Gonna give us back the price of admission?" Billows of laughter. Gold waited.

As the audience silenced the tension mounted. Like a magician waving a cape to produce an elephant out of thin air, Abe Gold waved his hands shouting, "Ladies and gentlemen, THE CLUTCHING HAND!"

The curtains parted and there was Sheldon Lewis standing against the white screen.

Not a sound, it was like the audience had been knocked cold by the heavyweight champion.

Sheldon eyeing Gold nervously. Why had he agreed to this damned silly appearance? Why? As a bag of popcorn landed at his feet he stopped asking.

But Gold was true to his word. Hand raised, the police, the ushers, and what looked like some people from the National Guard blocked off the aisles.

"Ladies and gentlemen. Let me now introduce a most gracious and charming man, Mr. Sheldon Lewis."

Lewis tried to recover himself. He was a handsome man. He'd played a few leads on the stage, but in the movies he was known only as a villain.

He pulled every string in his memory to look like Romeo or Antony or. . . .

Gold's voice almost sounded like the pipe organ. "Mr. Lewis is a kind and gracious man. He gives to charity. He loves little children and animals. He said to me just before he came on, 'I don't know why people hate me so'."

A hawking voice: "Because he's The Clutching Hand!"

There was a chorus of boos and hisses. And as Lewis stepped forward to make his speech an apple core hit him on the shoulder.

At the railway station, Gold and Lewis shook hands.

"It's been quite an experience," Lewis observed. "I never realized the power of the movies."

Abe Gold smiled and pulled at his right ear. "Let us hope, Mr. Lewis, in the decade to come a power for good."

Back at the Pathé studio, Sheldon Lewis finished telling about his hair-raising Chicago escapade.

"Even on the train, the people stared at me. It's incredible. Why?"

George Seitz sucked on his pipe.

"Over ten million watch you and Pearl all over the world, Sheldon, and no one knows why."

Pearl, walking away from a crap game with Pitch and Cuny, poked Sheldon's shoulder.

"Well, kid, next month I start a personal appearance tour. Any Advice?"

Lewis patting her hand.

"Take along a bodyguard."

"Hell, I'll make it two, I'm wearing my first mink coat—it cost me twenty thousand bucks!"

TO BE CONTINUED

Pearl White poses on the deck of the liner *La Savoie,* ready to sail to France (February 1922).

Pearl with Charles Cochran, landing in New York after a sixth-month stay in France.

Pearl is heading for the sky on a girder. The site is 42nd Street and Broadway, the date April 12, 1917. After Pearl came down from her tour of the
building under construction, she lectured the crowd that had gathered about
the virtues of enlisting in the Navy.

Pearl and Theodore Cozzika tour Egypt (*c.* 1930–1931).

Pearl digs for clams at her Bayside estate.

Pearl donned baseball garb in this 1914 scene.

Pearl arrives in Paris, 1924. (Courtesy *Cinemathèque Française*)

Pearl (with cane) arrives in Cairo, *c.* 1935.

Pearl gets fine reception on her arrival at Dover, England (1925) for *The London Revue*. (From the John Robyns collection.)

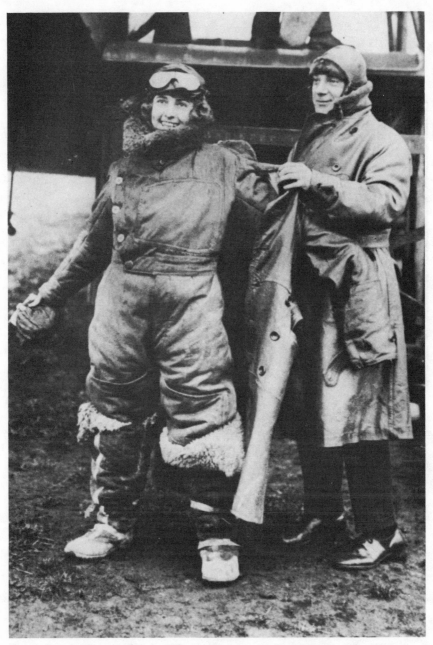

Pearl gets ready for a flight to Paris from Cricklewood, England.

Pearl gets into her Rolls, as her chauffeur sits by ready to take her into town. (*c.* 1917.)

Episode Five:

She Twilight Sleep

The train whistled off and the cars jerked and jolted and the grey misting twilight slowly drifted by like a ballet dancer's veil.

"Goodbye, K.C. Hello, St. Louie!"

Pearl waved at a circle of shadows outside the window and then slumped heavily in the seat as her French maid, Margarita, tipped the porter and closed the door of their compartment.

Her spirits should have been high. Her tour had been a tremendous success. Everywhere she had been welcomed by enthusiastic crowds though she hadn't needed any bodyguards. Some had shouted, "We love you Pearl!"

Had they meant it, really? How could anyone love a movie star?

Pressing her cheek against the cold glass she felt the rain patting the pane gently as though sorry for it. She pulled herself erect. Why this damned questioning? She had everything in the world.

She had risen from the deepest poverty to heights that promised untold riches. What the hell was the matter with her?

About to ask Margarita for a shot of Scotch, she shrugged the thought off and sagged back against the window, staring as the twilight blur thickened into darkness. And slowly as though in a half dream her childhood drifted before her.

"You were born in that one-story red brick house just back of the old livery stable. As Dad always said, since you never stopped kicking or hitting at something from your cradle, 'some of those wild mares must have marked you'."

Sister Grace had said this one night after Pearl had been quarreling with her father. All they ever did together was kick and bite with her getting most of the kicking where it hurt.

Why?

73

Edward G. White never could keep a job, nor could he keep his family in even the barest of necessities. His teenage wife, Elizabeth House, always seemed in the family way. First there was George. Then Opal, who died of diphtheria at three. And Grace, who was like their second mother. And then Fred, who ran away and eventually joined the Navy at sixteen. And last Pearl Fay White.

"Pearl Fay White. . . ." She said her name as though hearing it for the first time.

"Miss White, you want something?" It was Margarita, hovering above her.

"No, just thinking out loud."

Margarita settled down beside her.

"You know M, this Missouri land hatched me."

Margarita smiled, pulling some knitting from a large bag.

"I was born in Green Ridge, a little village of about 300, just a hop, skip and jump from Sedalia." She sighed deeply, staring into the racing-by night. "I wonder what it's like now?"

The train whistle was shrill and triumphant. Pearl sat up. Her face flushed, her eyes were flashing; she seemed more like her screen image.

"Margarita, I have a wonderful idea. It's on our way. A few hours won't make any difference. We'll stop over at Sedalia and then take a horse and buggy to Green Ridge, where we'll pay respects to my mother's grave."

Margarita's needles flashed in the half-light.

"I heard a priest once say it was good for the soul to look on the grave of a loved one at least once before we die. . . ."

"Mister, will you drive us by Wood's Opera House, Please?"

The buggy creaked and rocked as he turned out of the railroad station and headed for the center of Sedalia.

The sun beat down on the muddy road and a crisp breeze scattered leaves from the maples that lined the street.

Sedalia hadn't changed in fifteen years. It was sleepy and flat as a pancake where grain and cattle met for profit.

"There it is, there it is!"

Pearl jumped out and ran across the street to a two-story building whose front was crested by a canopy of stained glass that read, Wood's Opera House.

Margarita huffed and puffed beside her.

"M, here is where I was first bitten."

Margarita's eyes wide.

"Here one night my dad took us all to see *Uncle Tom's Cabin*. I was so enthralled I rose out of the seat and tried to go up to heaven with little Eva. I *was* little Eva in that inspiring moment and I vowed to be an actress no matter what Dad said and I knew he would say no."

Thunderheads rolled in the east as the buggy swung into the graveyard. Long shadows draped the headstones as a church bell tolled the noon hour. Slowly, Pearl and Margarita entered the cemetery.

An elderly gentlemen stepped out of a small wooden house and greeted them.

"May I help you, ladies?"

"Yes, sir. I'm Pearl White. I'm looking for my mother's grave. Her name is Elizabeth White.

He stepped back in the house and a few minutes later returned.

"Right this way."

The wind was rising and cold and splashes of rain shot through it. After stepping around and over headstones the old man halted before an unmarked grave.

"There it is, ma'am."

Pearl stared, not believing. There was not even the barest trace of a headstone—not even barest of necessities. Again her father's shadow fell ominously. Tears stung her eyes. She clenched her fists and almost swore. Margarita placed a warm hand on hers.

"I want a black marble stone placed here and I don't care how much it costs," Pearl snapped.

"Shall we say a prayer, Miss White?"

Pearl's skin burned. Pray? How long had it been since she prayed? Only at her stepmother Inez's demands had the White kids prayed or got the rod. Pray? She stepped closer to the grave.

Margarita knelt and crossed herself.

Pearl knelt and thought.

Dear Mother whom I never knew, dead at twenty-nine in childbirth hear me. Out of all the struggle and sadness, out of all the pain and anguish, out of the loneliness and want, it seems at last I've found a place for your little orphan. Help her to appreciate it, help her to help others in your name.

At the little house the old gentleman greeted them again.

"Sir I'll have a headstone made in St. Louis and shipped here," Pearl promised.

He nodded shakily. "That's fine, Miss White. Sometimes I feel awful sorry for those graves without any stone or name on 'em."

Margarita dabbed her eyes with a handkerchief.

"Also, would you see that some flowers are placed on my mother's grave once a month on a Friday, the day she died?"

The man nodded again as Pearl slipped a twenty dollar bill into his hand.

Pearl, choking back tears, stumbled toward the buggy.

As Margarita climbed in after she whispered: "I hope to God you brought the bottle."

TO BE CONTINUED

THE IRON CLAW

Two publicity stills for *The Iron Claw*. ("The Unknown" was Harry Fraser.)

The timely arrival of the police saves Janet (the girl being administered to; Pearl is on the right.)

Sheldon Lewis is featured in this scene from *The Iron Claw*. The girl was working as a spy, and is reporting the bad news that she has "blown her cover."

"Who Taught the Parrot to Speak?" We're not sure, but his words seem to have had a devastating effect upon the company assembled. (Pearl, of course, and Sheldon Lewis.)

Helene Chadwick points the accusing finger at Pearl. If she did commit the murder, though, it was surely in self-defense!

Here, Sheldon Lewis displays his "iron claw."

For The Stars and Stripes

As the New York crowd of 5,000 gasped, the girl on the girder reached the twentieth story of the Bush terminal building on West 42nd Street and showered them with hundreds of circulars.

A sea of hands grabbed at the papers.

"Hey, what's it say?"

A burly Irisher jumped up on the platform decorated with American flags and read: "JOIN UP FOR THE STARS AND STRIPES! WHIP THE HUN AND SAVE THE WORLD FOR DEMOCRACY!"

Applause and shouts and whistles followed. The girl and girder descended quickly.

Clad in military uniform she stepped off the steel beam and grabbed the Irisher's arm.

"I've done my bit—now you do yours!"

"It'll be a pleasure, me lassie. And may I ask the colleen's name?"

There was a broad smile and a shake of the blonde head.

"They call me Pearl White. What do they call you?"

Thunderous applause drowned out the Irisher's answer as the crowd surged forward and the Mayor shook Pearl's hand.

As the chauffeur-driven limousine sped away from the still cheering mob Pearl tapped the gentleman beside her on the shoulder and quipped:

"Well, Prince George the Loud, do you think I can top this?"

George Seitz smirked and tapped his knobby bamboo cane.

"I know where you can sell a bundle of Liberty Bonds."

"OK. Lead me to it."

"I'd say it's much more dangerous than this exploit."

"So what? Nothing I won't do to beat the Kaiser."

Seitz tweaked his nose and grinned.

"How about a drink over which we will plot our invasion of

the Union Club where the male elite gather for conversation and
games without benefit of the opposite sex?"

"No women?"

"No women. They even take an oath to it."

Pearl's smile was wide and eyes twinkled.

"To hell with the drink! Let's go. Uncle Sam is calling."

Pearl and Seitz crept beside a tall hedge.

"George, how am I going to get in?"

"Through the lounge window just around the corner."

Around the corner and in front of the open window George
made a platform of his hands and Pearl stepped on them. Slowly
she peered into the elegant tapestried room. There was a pervasive
haze of expensive cigar smoke. Several gentlemen were playing
chess. Others were reading. All was quite proper for the city's
most proper club.

"I'll count three and then in you go."

Pearl tapped him on the shoulder and braced herself.

"One . . . two . . . three!"

Pearl tumbled head first through the window onto a plush
divan, startling a pale-faced gentleman almost shocking pink and
forcing him to drop his drink on the Oriental rug.

"My God! Its a woman!"

"Call the police!"

"We'll never live this down!"

Gathering herself together Pearl smiled at the knot of men
pressing around her.

"Gentlemen, please hear me out."

There was much buzzing and head-wagging.

A distinguished gentleman stepped forward.

"My dear lady, we are gentlemen despite the fact our club is
taboo to your sex. You must admit your entrance was quite extra-
ordinary. You may explain before we take any action."

"Thank you, sir."

Adjusting her cap she moved to the center of the lounge.

"By the way, my name is Pearl White."

An ancient member giggled and repeated:

"Pearl White? What a pretty name. I once had a friend named
Ruby."

"Hush, Jerome, the lady is going to speak."

"As you all know we are at war with Germany. And our
country needs money to fight this monstrous enemy that has

ravaged most of Europe. Being a woman I can't carry a gun but I can carry the message to the people. Liberty Bonds are the backbone of our armies and fighting men. I ask your help to bring this glorious crusade to a smashing victory."

Shouts and cheers echoed through the room.

"What'd she say? Wants us to join up and fight the Germans? Bully idea. I'm ready."

One of the gentlemen stepped up and stuffed a twenty dollar bill in her hand. In quick succession bills and checks were handed to Pearl.

Taking off her military cap she filled it to overflowing.

"And now, Miss White, let us seal our union with a toast."

At the long mahogany topped bar Pearl lifted her glass.

"To our President Woodrow Wilson who gave us our standard —SAVE THE WORLD FOR DEMOCRACY!"

Shouts and cheers again: everyone burst into a verse of "Over There." As the tumult subsided the distinguished gentleman who had first spoken to Pearl shyly said:

"Miss White, we are most pleased at your patriotism and your visit.

"But what about our tradition? We've lost it. We'll never be the old Union Club again."

This was followed by whispers and drooping heads.

"Gentlemen, I may be a woman but I can keep a secret and yours shall go with me to my grave!"

There was clapping and one or two whistles as the gentlemen led Pearl to the exit.

"By the way, Miss White, what do you do?"

Pearl throwing back a broad smile.

"I fight the forces of evil in the flickers!"

There was a surging sigh as Pearl disappeared through the oak panel doors.

"Heavens! An actress! Do you think we can trust her to keep our tradition?"

"Well Louie, I raised ten thousand dollars in Liberty Bonds."

Kissing her hand, Gasnier drew up a chair beside his desk.

"And millions of more fans to storm the box-office."

Pearl banged the desk with her fist.

"Louie, don't you ever think of anybody but yourself?"

As he backed away from her, Pearl continued: "There's a world war on. Your own country and most of Europe have been devastated. And you think of box-office."

He smiled and bowed before her.

"Im sorry, *ma cherie*. I was only thinking of your career. Oh, by the way, did you see the little American flag I had hung over the entrance to the studio for our boys who've gone over there?"

Pearl slumped in the chair. "And what do *you* propose doing?" Pearl demanded of her producer.

Grabbing her hand dramatically, Gasnier protested, "You know, I would die for France! But since I am beyond the draft age——"

"How much?"

Startled, Gasnier lurched back.

"How much are you giving, Louie?"

Nervously he lit a cigarette. "Well, the returns on your last serial haven't come in yet . . . "

Pearl cracked her knuckles. "Don't give me that crap! *How much?*"

Slowly his cigarette drooped in his mouth. "Put us down for—for five thousand."

"OK. Write the check now since I'm reporting to the Liberty Bond people in the morning." The pen's scratching was the only noise breaking the heavy quiet. Gasnier's hand trembled as he extended the check to Pearl. Pearl started humming *La Marseillaise,* at the end of which she threw her legs on the desk, smiling from ear to ear.

"Now, may we talk business?" Louis pleaded.

Pearl nodded.

"I have the script for your new picture. Your last serial, *Pearl of the Army,* has been an inspiration to the boys in the trenches. But now to turn to something a bit different."

Rubbing his hands together, he continued:

"*The Fatal Ring!* Isn't that a great title? This time the villain will be a woman, Ruby Hoffman, who will play the high Priestess of the Secret Order of the Violet God. Warner Oland will also be a villain. All of them are trying to get the Violet Diamond of Darron from you. How does it sound?"

"It sounds great! Thank God I'm going to do a serial again. After those feature flops *Hazel Kirk, The King's Game,* and that last one, *Mayblossom,* I know I'm not for the heavy dramatic stuff. They were rotten as hell, but I didn't help them any."

"Oh, now, Pearl it was an experiment."

"Well, right now I want to devote all of my efforts to help

finish this damn war. My own personal life seems finished, so . . ."

A glint appeared in Gasnier's eye.

"I'm having a small dinner party tonight. Please come. Who knows; you may meet your future love?"

"You lecherous old bastard!"

"Please Pearl, it will do you good to meet new people."

"OK. But don't try and play cupid."

Gasnier glanced at his watch. Pearl was late again.

"Good evening, Major McCutcheon, pleased you could come. Where's Mr. Barrymore?"

The darkly handsome major in full British regalia brushed at his tight-lipped moustache.

"I called John but he had another engagement."

The front door opened and Pearl swept in, smothered in ermine.

"Sorry, Louie, even a Rolls Royce has a flat tire from time to time, and tonight we had one on Fifth Avenue."

Pearl's eyes wandered to McCutcheon, whose own eyes were sweeping her from head to foot. A little shiver went up her back. God, what a beautiful brute!

"Dinner is served."

Gasnier quickly introduced Pearl and McCutcheon and suggested they go into dinner together.

McCutcheon's arm pressed against her breast. And yet she didn't mind it.

As they moved towards their places Ruby Hoffman whispered to her.

"Watch out for this guy, he's a heart-breaker."

Pearl was wistful. "Mine was broken a long time ago."

TO BE CONTINUED

Pearl's first home—1022 W. Lynn, Springfield, Missouri. (*c*. 1900)

Pearl lived at 2058 N. Grant St. in Springfield, *c.* 1904.

Pearl first acted in the Diemer Theater, in Springfield.

Pearl went to this school in Green Ridge, Missouri, as a child.

Springfield, as it looked *c*. 1910.

Pearl's Bayside, New York, home *c.* 1919.

Pearl's home, Seine Et Oise Gazeran par Rambouillet, France (1930s).

Author Manuel Weltman pays tribute at Pearl White's grave, 1966. The grave is located in France.

She Perilous Plunge

Pearl let the pink satin robe drop to the black marble floor and stepped naked down into the huge white marble sunken tub as Margarita poured mixtures of sweet smelling salts and oils into the water. She splashed around like a kid in the ol swimmin' hole.

Floating on her back she said dreamily: "Who'd a thought little poverty Pearl from Green Ridge, Mo., would some day have an apartment on 42nd and Broadway, and a water closet that would have made Cleopatra envious."

"With all the Egyptian motif who'd think the queen of the Nile *had* lived here?" Margarita added.

"That's why I call it Little Egypt."

"But the boudoir—mirrors wall to ceiling. I don't know how you can wake up with all those Pearl faces looking down at you, and be so calm."

"I'm an egomaniac, like John Barrymore who formerly owned the apartment. John was so in love with himself he wanted to perform and watch at the same time."

Pearl walked out of the shining bowl, scattering water everywhere until Margarita threw a towel over her and started drying her.

Pearl giggled.

"I'll never forget what W. C. Fields said about the bathroom when I threw my first party. 'Well, Pearl Girl, it's a veritable heaven for heaving and peeing, except for one dilemma.' 'And what's that W.C.? I said.' 'Since most of your friends are actors, I suggest you have two toilets. One for just people, the other for Thespians who eat asparagus'."

Pearl and Margarita guffawed.

"So its Major McCutcheon again tonight?"

"Its our eighth straight date since I met him at Gasnier's.

We're going out to dine and dance at Bayshore."

Pulling the rubber cap off her head she slid over to the mirror that made up the bathroom door.

"I've never seen you so serious about a man."

"He's different, M. He doesn't push me though I know he's interested. He acts as though he wants me to make the first pass, which I think is cute for such a virile built guy."

Surveying her body: "Guess I've still got the mark of the tomboy my early show business days stamped on me."

She ran her hands over her breasts, her belly, her thighs and then posed like a Mack Sennett Bathing Beauty.

"He makes me feel like a woman."

Margarita handed her her underthings. "Miss Pearl White, I never heard anybody say you weren't."

Pearl, brushing her cheek with a kiss, ran into the bedroom and sat before the triangular shaped mirror framed in crystal.

Putting on her make-up: "Since my teen age marriage-blowup with Victor, I've never thought I could find a man who'd help me build a home and a family."

Margarita appeared behind her with the blonde wig, but Pearl waved it away: "No, M., I'm not going to wear it tonight. Tonight I want Wally to see the real Pearl."

Lining her eyebrows: "You know, I can't always be a movie star. Some day old age or booze will catch up with me. I'd like someone I could warm my cold feet with."

Rouging her lips: "M., what do you think of Wally?"

Margarita's cheeks reddened. She had heard things about the English playboy actor and his women. How could she tell her? Besides, a woman in love believes what she wants to believe. She pressed her hand over Pearl's.

"He's certainly handsome and dashing. But with the possibility of him going overseas I'd advise you to wait."

Pearl flushed: "Oh, I wasn't thinking of anything like marriage—I mean—at least until after he returns."

Margarita was setting the star's brown hair. "Who knows what the war will bring for anyone," she went on. "Or for the whole world?"

The door chimes rang: "There he is. Punctual as all-get-out."

Pearl slipped into a shimmering beaded evening gown: "For the first time I'm having fun. Maybe that's all he wants."

A white ermine cape over her shoulders she stared at her reflection in a full length mirror.

"I've never seen you so beautiful, Miss White," Margarita smiled.

"I hope Wally thinks so. I'll go to the door. And don't you wait up."

"Good evening, Pearl," her guest greeted her.

"Good evening yourself. Would you like a drink?"

"I can wait."

McCutcheon stared blankly at her.

"Well, do you like it? I bought this dress for tonight. I didn't think it would tie your tongue."

He brushed his moustache with a finger and forced a smile.

"It's not the dress—it's your hair. What have you done with it?"

Pearl, hands on hips, stared back. "Not a thing."

She stepped closer to him.

"I thought you knew I wore a wig. The wig made me a movie star. When I want to be 'just me,' I go natural. And, Wally, I want more than anything in the world to be that for you tonight."

His arms closed about her. "But, Pearl, no one will recognize you. What about your public? You are a great star. You have a tradition to live up to."

The veins in her throat swelled, the blood rushed to her temples, her eyes flashed. "To hell with tradition!"

She turned away quickly and going to the bar poured herself a quick one. Looking back she saw he was waiting for her to make the next move.

Damn him! But that's what attracted her.

"If it means that much to you I'll put the damn wig on!"

As she swept past him to the bedroom he caught her arm and swung her to him.

"I'm sorry I offended you. You see, I've fallen under the spell of whom I thought was an unattainable star, and to know she is also a fascinating woman was too much to expect."

His lips were heavy upon her's, his tongue was deep in her mouth.

No one had ever kissed her like that.

She returned it.

Pulling herself away she picked up her gold evening bag and handed him some car keys.

"I thought we'd take the Stutz tonight. Care to drive?"

"Love it."

The pleasure in his eyes pleased her. So he did have *other* violent delights. OK Pearl, this peril is for real.

Like ghostly figures Pearl and Wally made circles on the terrace, the moonlight sifting from misty clouds above them. The roar of the waves was strangely remindful of cannon as the hit tune of the war, "Roses of Picardy," drifted from the dance floor.

As the last strains were drowned out by the bay-waters, Wally kissed her gently on the lips. Tears misting her eyes, Pearl clung desperately to him.

"Let it go on forever, let it."

"Tonight will be ours forever, darling, tonight."

His kiss smothered her mouth.

"Wally, let's go wading on the beach."

"Very well, my mermaid."

Shoes and stockings off they frolicked as children frolic, and laughed as children laugh in the waves.

"Wonder what your commanding officer would say now if he saw you?"

Wally was dusting the sand from his feet with a handkerchief. "He'd say—Major Wallace McCutcheon, you sail tomorrow for combat."

"Oh, dear God, no!"

"Yes, Pearl, I received my orders this morning. I didn't want to tell you like this, but——"

For a moment they sat on the rocky ledge like statues watching the waves breaking themselves into a thousand diamonds.

Suddenly Pearl was in his arms kissing his eyes and ears and mouth, devouring his breath.

"Pearl, you don't really want me to——"

"Yes, darling, yes. You said tonight was ours forever."

"But, dearest, with the war and everything——"

"That's why, Wally."

Pearl was holding his cheeks between her hands, not holding the tears back from her eyes.

"I love you, you bully Britisher. And I can't do a damn thing about it."

Their bodies rolled together on the sand.

Like a peeping Tom the moon watched from between the black clouds. . .

TO BE CONTINUED

Dressed in military garb, and as a civilian, for *Pearl of the Army*.

Pearl and Ralph Kellard affect look of injured innocence as fisticuffs break out.

Soldier Ralph Kellard is getting a send-off from Pearl. (The John Robyns Collection)

Pearl and Ralph on the alert.

Pearl looks on from a position of comfort as military strategy is discussed. Or is that strategy exactly military?

Pearl poses here as though she were modelling for an equestrienne statue.

Ralph subdues evil-doer, to the delight of Pearl and her servants.

The army brass once again pauses to talk things over.

Pearl has the drop on Ralph Kellard here.

Episode Eight:

Heights of Hazards

"What are the fines imposed on my people?"

The burly Sheriff put down the official looking book.

"For cruelty to animals—in your case, a horse—it's two dollars apiece."

Seitz and company exchanged startled glances. A few bills showed up but not enough for the fine for twenty-five. Finally Pearl pulled off her wig, shouting:

"My God, I've just bought a fourteen thousand dollar Rolls Royce and a quarter million dollar mansion in Bayside, Long Island and I haven't got two bucks to help spring us from the clink!"

She burst up to the Sheriff.

"I want to call the head of our company, Sheriff."

The Sheriff raised his hands as everyone pressed forward.

"Everybody into the cell! Jerry, show these folks the way."

Pearl grabbing his shoulder.

"But we have a right to make one phone call."

"Follow my deputy, folks, follow my deputy. You too, Miss."

"But Sheriff, I must make a phone call."

"Miss, you get in that cell before I handcuff you."

As the doors clanked and Pearl fumed behind the bars the hot August sun turned the Milford, Pennsylvania, jail into a furnace.

"Miss White, I don't know what to say about what happened."

Dick LaMarr, who doubled most of the dangerous stunts for Pearl, sidled up to her sheepishly.

"Dick, I saw the whole thing. When you reached for that overhanging limb to swing off the horse his right rear leg hit a soft shoulder. That's what tumbled him down the embankment. And he got only a scratch for it."

"But why did the Sheriff fine all you people? If I was cruel to Jocko why fine you?"

"These small towns have to make revenue somehow. And to think Pathé paid that old bastard to keep the natives away during the chase scene."

Frank Leon Smith, a scenario writer, quipped.

"That's what you call a two-way take."

Seitz turned to his bewildered cohorts.

"I'm sure the Sheriff will let us make the call to the studio. Let's just relax and wait."

Smith handed Pearl a cigarette through the bars.

"Pearl, when are we going to start writing your biography. You know you have a six-month deadline."

"This is a helluva time to talk to me about my life story. God, I wish I had a drink!"

Pitch looked up from his sitting position on the floor.

"Pitch, you haven't?"

"I have. Here!"

He produced a half-pint flask and handed it to Pearl, who took a long pull. As she passed the flask through the bars to Smith.

"Pearl, I didn't know you bought a place in Long Island. Could it be a honeymoon cottage?"

"Maybe. Boy, I sure miss that guy. These last months have been like years. Oh, I wish this war would end."

The crowded cell suddenly quiet as everyone was alone with his thoughts.

The Sheriff came lumbering up.

"Miss, I called your studio. They're sending the bail by Western Union money order. There's a Mister Gas on the phone who wants to talk to you."

As Pearl went through the door she smirked over her shoulder to Smith:

"If that isn't a perfect description of the master of Pathé— Mister Gas!"

"Now Pearl, this is the way the action goes. You've been captured by the Priestess of the Sacred Order of the Violet God, and you're being held in the temple. You'll be bound hand and foot, a rope tied to your feet will go to that pulley on that rafter and from there to a cleat on the wall. Now the henchmen of the Priestess roll in a huge iron cauldron, mounted on wheels and boiling with melted lead. Its ray illuminating your face as——"

Pearl interrupted.

"As I hang head down. Gad, Prince George the Loud, can't I ever do a bluejean without my head down?"

Crew laughed.

Seitz motioned her over to the kettle.

"Come over here Pearl; look at the ingenious way Pitch and the boys made this. Look, the kettle has a false bottom halfway up. The top section is filled with water, and sulfur pots burning below the surface produce furious bubbles and smoke fumes. In the bottom section is a strong arc light. Its ray will shine upward through a plate glass in the false bottom. What do you think of it?"

"You said it George, ingenious." Turning: "Oh, Pitch, you inspect the ropes and see to the knots. I'll never forget that time in *Pauline* when I fell on my head. Maybe that's why I can do these madcappers—no brains."

Everyone laughed again as they began setting up the scene.

"By the way George, I think you're slipping. Are you going to have the henchmen just cut the rope?"

Seitz grinned. "You know me better than that. I sit up half my nights thinking of better ways to dispose of you. How about this?" They relaxed in chairs behind the camera. "The Priestess really gets mean now," Seitz explained. "She has the henchmen rub raw meat on the rope and while some of them hold the rope taut to keep you from dropping, the others feed the rope through a cage filled with ferrets and then tie the rope to the wall."

Pearl interrupted. "I get it;. the ferrets, smelling the raw meat, go wild and start gnawing like mad on the rope. I hang head down helpless as the rope is shredded thinner and thinner and the pot boils higher and higher."

Seitz continued. "A final close-up: the ferrets bite through the rope, the last strand parts, a quick flash of you falling . . . TO BE CONTINUED!"

Pearl clapped him on the back. "Gad, George, you must be smoking opium along with that Scotch you gargle. Well Pitch, let's get knotted up."

Pitch sauntered over as the cameraman nodded to Seitz that everything was ready for the take.

"Cut!"

Pitch rushed over and started to poke a stick into the cage. Pearl, head down, yelled: "What the hell is going on?"

Pitch laughed.

"What the hell's so funny, Pitch? Let me in on it so I can laugh myself to death."

"We started out with two ferrets. Now we got six. One musta been a mother."

Howls of laughter rocked the studio. Pearl shouted. "Stop making me laugh so hard, I've got enough blood rushing to my head."

After the shot Pearl relaxed on a couch as Margarita brought her a cup of coffee.

"Miss Pearl White?"

"Yes," Pearl said, staring up at a young man in a Western Union uniform.

"Cablegram for you, please sign here."

Her heart was beating furiously as she signed. Hesitating for a moment she suddenly tore the cable open and read:

DEAR PEARL,
    HAVE NOT WRITTEN BECAUSE I WAS WOUNDED AND HOSPITAL-
    IZED AND
    THEN UNDERWENT SURGERY—STOP—HOPE YOU CAN STILL
    LOVE A
    CHAP WITH A SILVER PLATE IN HIS HEAD—STOP—BACK TO
    STATES
    IN A WEEK OR TWO—STOP—LOVE WALLY

TO BE CONTINUED

PEARL'S FAMILY

Here are three rare photographs of two of Pearl's relatives.

Two views of Pearl's father, Edward White, during a visit in 1919 to Pearl's Bayside estate. (The John Robyns Collection)

Pearl's sister Grace, as she looked at the age of eighteen.

The Tell-Tale Heart

Brakes screeching! Tires shrieking! Horn squalling!

"My God, he's off again!"

"You mean Wally's making all that racket?" Sister Grace asked as she poured lemonade from a pitcher on the marble-topped table.

"Yes, almost every day he goes to the races."

Grace adjusted the umbrella above them to ward off the noonday sun.

"This last year of our marriage he's spent more time charging around in my Stutz and betting those nags than with me."

Sipping from glass, Pearl grimaced. "What the hell's this, Grace?"

"Lemonade. You used to drink it by the barrel when you were a kid."

"I need something with legs on it. Ring that bell for Gunner, will you dear?"

Two small boys running across the lawns that swept to the edge of the bay stopped when they heard the bell ringing. They listened and then rushed up to their mother, firing questions about what it was ting-alinging for.

"I'm calling for the butler. Your Aunt Pearl wants something. And here's some lemonade to cool you off."

The boys wiped their brows with their handkerchiefs.

"And your faces are red as beets. Now, go sit under that big tree and drink slowly."

Just then Gunner, a tall Swede, came from the house. "You rang, Madame?"

"Yes, Gunner. Bring me a double Scotch and tell Christine just a salad for our lunch."

As he turned to leave, Pearl called after him: "Make it a bottle instead, and some ice."

"Mama, why does the water never stop down there?"

"It keeps rolling in and in. And where does it roll from?"

Grace smiled at her sons Billy and Eddie.

"Only God knows that boys."

As they moved away, Eddie said:

"Maybe if we don't skip our prayers we can ask *him.*"

Pearl lit a cigarette, watching them. Her frown was becoming replaced by a half smile.

"They're adorable. Worth a dozen careers."

A breeze from the bay braved the waves of heat falling away from the stately old mansion.

"It's been wonderful having you here this past month."

Grace patting her sister's hand. "It's the first vacation I've ever had in my life—thanks to you. I don't know how the boys and I will be able to leave tomorrow."

Gunner appeared with the bottle and ice.

Grace's eyes narrowed as she watched her beautiful sister take a quick drink. How she had changed! So beautiful and exciting! And everytime she lifted a hand or said a word the world seemingly waited on her. But was she happy?

"Pearl, I don't want to pry. But is something wrong with Wally? I see how he acts so—so strange with the servants and even with you. Is he completely recovered from his wounds?"

Pearl took another shot. "He's not the same since the war. Of course he got that plate in his head. But it doesn't keep him from galavanting all over town. If it's not the races, it's the Lambs Club. Or a round of all-night gambling with Barrymore and his Broadway crowd."

"Well, dear, Loy and I had some rough moments our first six months. It takes time to learn to share your freedom with another person. I think it was the birth of Billy that straightened us out."

Pearl poured another drink. "I found when I was married to Victor I could never have a child."

The rollers on the rocks broke the sweating silence.

Suddenly there were shouts from the boys as they raced across the lawn to the tennis court where they jumped up and down on the net.

"Maybe I should have waited, Grace. But I felt so sorry for Wally, and he seemed to need me. He was in a helluva shape. I guess I thought I was another Florence Nightingale."

Gunner came towards them again.

"Madame, Mr. George Seitz on the telephone."

Pearl took the call in the library.

"Hi there, Prince George the Loud. . . . Fine. . . . Just visiting with my sister and her boys. . . . What I wanted to ask you George was, could you write a part in for Wally. . . . Well, he's at sixes and sevens and maybe if we work together it'll straighten him out. After all he's been an actor all his life. I don't see why he can't go over in flickers. . . . Thanks, so much, George. See you next week."

Turning to leave, the phone rang again.

"Hello, . . . Wally. What's wrong? . . . You what? . . . Well, that'll be a few bucks you won't waste on those fillies. . . . What? . . . For Christ's sake, Albin is my chauffeur not an errand-boy! Why can't you come and get it? . . . Oh, I see, some important people."

She held the receiver away from her ear fuming.

"OK, I'll send him. Where is this dive?"

She scrawled on the phone-pad.

"Will you be home for dinner? . . . Well, will you be home—period?"

Slamming the phone she called for Gunner.

"Gunner, Major McCutcheon forgot his wallet. He's at a speakeasy. Will you have Albin take it to this address?"

"Yes, Madame."

Pearl watched Grace and the boys. She listened to the laughter and happy play, and then to her own heart. Oh, dear God, *had* she made a mistake?

Why had she listened to her heart and not her head? Maybe if Wally worked with her—maybe.

Grace stood in the doorway of Pearl's luxurious bedroom decorated in the style of Louis XVI. It was exquisite and Pearl was too, lying on that golden bed. Grace tiptoed across the white carpet and stood looking down at her sister.

What a brave and courageous child Pearl had been: facing up to their father—even when he had a strap in his hand; adjusting to the sternness of their step-mother, Inez—even to little things like Inez's forbidding them even to touch a needle on Sunday. When she caught her sewing, Pearl flabbergasted her by holding up a nail and not a needle.

Pearl opened her eyes slowly; Grace's figure seemed to float in the late afternoon shadows that reached like veils across the room.

"Grace, how long have you been there?"

Grace sat down on the bed. "Just a few moments. I was remembering."

"Remembering? What?" Pearl lit a cigarette.

"Our childhood. And about you smoking a cigarette in one of Harry Leonard's plays."

Pearl sat up laughing.

"I thought Papa would burst a blood vessel watching you smoke in public."

Pearl bounced off the bed, imitating her father: "I'd rather see you dead than act another part on that infernal stage!

"I absolutely forbid you to continue this degrading life."

Grace imitated Pearl: "But Father, its all I want to do. And pretty soon I'll be leaving home and traveling all over the country. And someday I'll be in New York in a Broadway show."

Pearl continued the imitation: "How dare you defy me! I'll see Judge Lincoln and obtain a restraining order. That's what I'll do!"

Pearl and Grace laughed as they hugged each other.

"And he tried, oh, how he tried! But the judge said when I was eighteen I could do as I pleased and since I'd be of age soon why make such a fuss."

"Oh, Pearl, how I've envied your ambition. When I think of what you had to overcome, it's hard to believe."

Ella, the maid, brought in coffee.

"Where are the boys?" Pearl suddenly asked.

"Napping, just like you've been."

Pearl sipped the coffee. "That's the first time in years I've done that. My routine is so hectic I hardly know what sleep is. That's why I—I drink."

As Ella slipped out, Grace turned to Pearl: "Oh, Pearl, did I tell you Dr. Diemer passed away."

"Dr. Diemer? What memories he brings back. Patent medicines, his cold cure tables—what did he call them—Anti-Grippine, and an ankle corset. And to round out his money-making schemes, he owned the only theatre in town."

"It's still there. May Evans wrote me she never misses your serials. The whole town turns out."

Grace refilled their cups. "Nothing like a good cup of coffee," she observed.

Pearl stared at her sister. "I know what you're trying to say, dear. I know it myself. I drink too much. I'm even gaining weight.

George's wife's been taking me to a gym but exercise and sweats don't seem to remove a pound. Guess I'll have to wear those rubber bloomers to squeeze me thin for my next film."

Grace held both Pearl's hands. "I've never been against drink except when it's used as a prop. Like in one of your movies. It's not real, honey, and it may let you dream for awhile but then nightmares are sure to come."

Pearl got up, lit another cigarette and began pacing the room. "Dr. Diemer gave me my first paying job. He had a printing press that turned out his circulars, ads and the posters, and programs for the theatre upstairs. I hand fed the press. That's how I meet Harry Leonard and got my first real part in a stock company."

Pearl stared out the French windows, looking down at the sea, which seemed more a painting than reality. "Frances Fields, one of the leading ladies, took a liking to me, coached and advised me. What a mad schedule I had that one year. During the day I'd sweat over the press, at night I'd study the lessons Miss Fields wrote out for me and then act in the small parts I qualified for. And I received the fantastic sum of fifty cents a performance. With the pay from Dr. Diemer I paid Miss Fields, gave some to Inez and put a little away for myself."

Moving back into the middle of the stunning bedroom she waved her hands around. "And now I sleep in a room that cost five thousand to furnish!"

"Pearl, you deserve every penny."

"Grace, I want to do something for Dad. How about buying Inez and him a house? Think ten thousand would get them a nice place?"

Tears welled in Grace's eyes as she put her arms around Pearl and kissed her tenderly on the cheek.

"Only *you* could forgive and forget that much."

Pearl poured the coffee this time.

"Well, dear sister, before my halo gets any bigger, I have a confession to make. Remember when I got you a part in *The Prisoner of Zenda*?"

"Yes, I was so scared I thought I'd get sick to my stomach when I went on that stage. But it was funny—I didn't. I just became someone else."

"And so you might have been. Mr. Leonard wanted you to go with us. But I talked him out of it. You see, dear sister, I was afraid if you joined the company my chances would be cut in half."

"Oh, you little goose!" Grace whacked her playfully on the fanny.

There was a knock on the door.

"Come in. . . . Yes, Gunner. What is it?"

"Miss White, it's the police. There's been a raid. Major Mc-Cutcheon is in jail!"

TO BE CONTINUED

THE FATAL RING

Warner Oland, in his pre-Charlie Chan days, enters room to find sinister figures with drawn guns . . . and our heroine, of course.

Pearl ponders her fate as her two guards ponder her.

Warner Oland seems ready to order Pearl's execution. It didn't take place, of course.

The gentleman reluctantly turns the ring over to Pearl.

Pearl and Earle Fox look in on Mrs. Spencer Bennet. Does she imagine the ring is in that vase?

Warner Oland thought he was going to win. But as usual truth and justice prevail. Maybe that's why Warner switched to the other side later on in his career.

Episode Ten:

Webs of Deceit

"Here comes the rain again. Let's head for that barn over there."

Pearl and Frank Leon Smith ran up from the cliff while the rest of the company scattered to get out of the downpour. Inside Pearl and Smith lit cigarettes.

"Well, let's get on with your biography. Only about three chapters to go. Incidentally, the publisher liked what I sent him. But he suggested a new title—*Just Me*."

Pearl took off her wet shoes.

"*Just Me*—what's that supposed to mean?" She smirked.

"I sometimes wonder."

Pearl frowned.

"Well Pearl, one time you tell me one story and the next time you tell another. I thought you said 'nothing but the truth'."

Pearl pulled off her stockings and hung them to dry on a shovel propped against the wall.

"I tell the truth—most of the time. Just retouch the facts a little. Besides, who wants to read about a kid walking seven miles to pick berries for sixty cents a day to help support her family?"

"Everybody. It's a great human story. It shows what you overcame to be a big star. And it can inspire others."

Pearl put a finger on her chin and gave a little girl's curtsy.

"Next you'll have me saying I had visions like Joan of Arc."

Smith sharpened his pencil with his pocket knife.

"I'll bet you don't remember the story you told me about that anklet you always wear."

Pearl said dramatically: "It was hand-riveted on by an Italian Count to seal our eternal moment of love."

Smith caught a glint in her big brown eyes.

"Cut the crap! You bought it at the Five and Ten."

"No, Tiffany's!"

"Now, Pearl, if that isn't juggling the truth."

Rain beat furiously on the roof; wind was whistling across the earthen floor, and a clap of thunder shook the walls.

Cuny pushed in the doors.

"Well, folks, looks like we're washed out for the day."

Pearl put on her shoes and stockings. "Why not continue this over at that little inn just before we get to Fort Lee?"

"Pearl, you sort of skimped on your first marriage. How about your second?"

She chewed on a French roll. "Wally's not only out of my book, but practically out of my life."

She threw the roll on the plate. "After the way he acted at the studio—trying to run everybody, even telling George how to direct, and embarrassing the hell out of me, what do you except? And that raid—in the Speakeasy—caught with two whores!"

"But Pearl, everybody will wonder why such a sought-after woman shies away from what many believe is the most important part of her life. And what about Victor, your first husband?"

"Victor is doing very well on Broadway. We had our differences. He didn't want me to go into movies. But I was forced to when I lost my voice."

"I didn't know you had any voice trouble."

"Well, screaming in those melodramas did something to my vocal cords. I couldn't project to the gallery. And after awhile my voice became so bad, I just had to give up the stage altogether. Never did get it back right. But I don't want to go into all that, so Victor's out too."

"If that's what you want."

"Frank, let's go now. Hope you won't mind dropping me off at Bayside."

As they started to leave the booth the plump waitress blocked off their exit.

"Would you folks like some dessert?"

"No, may I have the check Miss?"

As Smith helped Pearl on with her sealskin coat the waitress stared wide-eyed.

"Oh, you're Pearl White—the movie star!"

Pearl nodded amused.

"Oh, Miss White my little boy Axminster just loves you. He'd even miss a meal, and he's almost a glutton to put it mildly, to see your serials. If he could just have your autograph."

"I'd be most happy. How about on the menu?"

The waitress gushed.

"Oh, then he can have his two greatest loves—food and you!"

As they sped alongside the 6th Avenue El Smith asked: "Pearl, what about all these rumors that Pathé's in trouble?"

Pulling the tam off with one hand, and the wig with the other, she let the wind stream through her hair. "Ah, you know Gasnier and his business deals. As for me, I've just signed with William Fox to do ten features."

"I thought you hated features."

"I made one try, so why not another? I'm getting a helluva price and choice of script, director and the whole works, which Gasnier wouldn't agree to."

The skies cleared as Smith drove into Bayside.

"Come on in for a drink-Frank."

"I'll take a raincheck, Pearl. I'll see you tomorrow."

As he helped her out of his Packard: "Pearl, you mean a lot to millions of people—don't let anyone destroy that image."

She kissed him on the cheek and ran into the darkened mansion.

At the bar she poured a double. Where were the servants? She smiled, remembering it was their day off. And Wally? She stared into the twilight.

Both cars were in the garage. Well, a good hot bath and sleep, she hoped.

Slowly she mounted the stairway to the second floor. The shadows fell awkwardly about her. She felt a little dizzy, tired maybe. Or maybe the alky was getting to her.

As she opened her bedroom door she saw two naked bodies writhing on her golden bed.

She stared not believing. She grabbed for her breath. She thought she would faint for the first time in her life. She let the tears speak the words of hate welling in her mouth.

Closing the door she stumbled down the stairway and out to the garage.

TO BE CONTINUED

CHILDREN AND DOGS

Children and dogs may have been the nemesis of some of Hollywood's stars, but Pearl was not one of them. Here she is shown in several candid shots featuring her terrier Happy and some young friends of hers on her Long Island estate.

Episode Eleven:

The Hour of Three

Pearl groped her way down the dimly lit stairs of the El Fey Club on 45th Street. Suddenly a spotlight blinded her and a brassy voice blared out: "Hello, sucker! Texas Guinan welcomes you!"

Pearl struggled behind the head waiter to cross the jam-packed circular dance floor. Quickly engulfed by bodies of all sizes and shapes she waved her hand for help. Again the brassy voice blared above the smoke-filled room and bouncing turkey trot music.

"Over here, Pearl. Sit at my table."

Out of breath she slumped beside the big blonde gal, who glittered with diamonds from head to foot. Ordering champagne she watched Texas sip coffee.

"Well, honey, see you finally got rid of that Major mishap of your life."

Pearl forced a grin. "I heard *you* were in court too. Somebody said you had the band play 'The Prisoner's Song' when they carted you off to the pokey."

"Hell, yes. And I composed a ditty in honor of Judge Thomas, who acquitted me:

> Judge Thomas said, "Tex, do you sell booze?"
> I said, "Please don't be silly,
> I swear to you my cellar's filled
> With chocolate and vanilly."

Both women laughed heartily as the champagne arrived, served in a bottle labeled "Ginger Ale."

"Say, Texas, how come you're sporting that diamond bracelet with the gold police whistle on it? A new boyfriend?"

"Not on your life. I just bought it as a companion for my necklace of gold padlocks. You see, I've added another since the 'revenooers' put a six-month padlock on my last club."

Texas stood up, raising her hands for silence. The dancers stumbled off the floor to the tables as the band struck a loud chord.

"Now, I give you the Guinan Girls!"

Loud applause as eight scantily dressed girls, lips heavily rouged, high-kicked out of the shadows, just narrowly missing the patrons' heads as they went into "Give Us a Little Kiss, Will, Ya Huh?"

At the end of the song each girl spotted a bald-headed man and placed a gooey red smacker on their shining pates. The crowd went wild. And Texas shouted above it:

"Give the little girls a big hand!"

As they rushed off Texas banged the bedlam down with an empty "ginger ale" bottle.

"Anyone for leap frog?"

A balding gentleman nearing seventy staggered up to volunteer, and he and Texas leapfrogged around the floor.

Texas, back at the table, smiled down at Pearl.

"My God, girl, how do you do it? Where do you get all that energy? And night after night!"

Sipping her everpresent cup of coffee, Texas replied; "I love to see people happy, and sometimes making fools of themselves in public is the best way to do it—especially with some prohibition likker under their belts."

Looking over the milling crowd, Texas spotted a friend. "Hey, here comes Winnie Lightner. . . . Hello, sucker!"

"Hello, sucker yourself! Guess what?"

"What?"

"The Lightner Sisters and Alexander have just been booked into the Palace. What do you think of that?"

All three gals hugged each other.

"I knew you'd make it kid. You're the funniest comedienne in the business. Pearl, she'd laugh the pants off a scarecrow. How 'bout a song, Winnie?"

"But I don't have my music."

"My guys can play anything. You name it."

"OK, let's try 'White Pants Willie' on your geniuses!"

Texas announced Winnie and the band went into the tune.

Winnie Lightner—mugging, eye-rolling, falsettoing, baritoning, pratfalling—tore the song and the patrons apart. The crowd went wild at the conclusion.

Rushing back to the table, Winnie made her excuses:

"Gotta run, Texas. Folks at home don't know the good news. But I just had to tell you." The patrons were still clapping wildly as she dashed out.

Texas stood up in the middle of the floor. "Now, my butter and egg men, here's the most sensational dancer to come out of Egypt since Salome tossed off her veils for John the Baptist's head. I give you ISHTAR and her boa, MOSES."

Drums beat, bells tinkled, flutes whistled, and a beautiful gold-clad dark-haired girl with a twelve foot boa constrictor tossed around her neck slithered onto the floor. There were screams and squeals from a few lady patrons, and hoots and hollers from some of the males. But the dancer circled the floor to a rising tempo that almost burst the El Fey's walls.

In a whirling climax she swung the boa around and around the electrified audience until the drums crashed and she dropped face down on the floor.

Slowly the boa coiled around her and nestled against her as the amber spot faded and a roar rocked every glass and bottle on the square tables.

"Well, Texas, think I'll head for home." Pearl said yawning.

"It's almost closing. How about me fixing us some ham and——?"

Pearl nodded.

As the crowd began to thin out Broadway's rising gossip columnist, Walter Winchell, headed for Texas's table.

"Tex, that snake-dancer is fantastic. But who's going to eat any food while a snake hips around?"

"Walter, they come here to drink—not eat. Besides, I got a crush on Moses. He sleeps in a basket under the desk in my office."

As Texas poured drinks for Pearl and Winchell, the columnist inquired, "Well, La White, how does it feel to be single?"

"Great; marriage was a mistake I shall never make again. You can quote me."

"Anything else for my 'Stage Whispers'?"

"Yes, I've just finished my ten-feature-films contract with Fox. Most of 'em, sorry to say, were flops."

"Wait a sec, kiddo, don't knock my favorite movie star," Texas interrupted.

Winchell wrote on a pad. "But why didn't you do serials for Fox?"

"That's what he thought he could do. But you see, Walter, I have a lifetime contract with Pathé. I can't make serials for anybody else."

Winchell winked, "Shrewd business head under that blonde wig."

Texas put her arm around Pearl. "You can say that again. And why not? These producers will steal you blind."

"Well, enough of America. Tex, Walter, I have some really great news. Sometime ago Jacque-Charles, who is the Ziegfeld of Paris, visited with me and signed me to star in his review at the Casino de Paris. I sail for France in a week."

Texas mugged: "Oui, oui, baby. Don't let those froggies change our girl."

Winchell turned to Texas: "Anything new from your corner, champ?"

"No, just remind the suckers I haven't raised my prices like some others. I still charge only twenty-five dollars per head and two dollars for a pitcher of water. You can wash your pinkies or mix it with anything you want."

"Well, almost five A.M. Good slumber, ladies, I'll see you in print."

Winchell disappeared into the smoky gloom.

The soaring silence in the club caught onto every last step, giggle and curse up the stairs and into the grey dawn.

The clink of glasses . . . a final blow through a saxophone . . . a broom brushing streamers across the battered dance floor, trying desperately to hold back the locking of the doors . . . the shadows waiting in the corners for a runaway against the rising sun. . . .

"Good night, suckers." The brassy voice was soft now.

"Well, Pearl, have a nightcap while I get my apron on."

"For a change I'll try your java."

In the kitchen the gals busied over eggs and toast.

Sitting down to the warm-smelling breakfast, Texas said: "Pearl, I know how the Major got to you. And its not easy to forget—just like that." She snapped her fingers. "I've had a couple of outs in the marriage game myself. But time will heal like it does everything—even death."

Pearl sipped the coffee: "Thanks, Texas, for your advice. It's just that I wonder if I will always have to be alone? Alone at the top—with everything at your feet—is hard to take. Sometimes I want to be just anybody—as long as I'm with somebody."

The dawn silence was broken by the wheels of a milktruck. "We all pay a price for what we struggle for, Pearl. Stars like you —sometimes its bigger than life itself."

As they finished the meal, Texas extended an invitation: "Pearl, you know I always go to morning mass at St. Patrick's. It sort of cleans me up for the next night. How would you like to come?"

Pearl flushed: "I've never been much of a churchgoer."

Texas took her hand. "Honey, He doesn't keep tab on your visits to Him."

The Rolls Royce stopped at the entrance to St. Patrick's Cathedral. The two women slowly mounted the steps, their shadows draping behind them. Suddenly the rising sun impaled a spark on one of the steeples, lighting up the gloom, and frightening the shadows away.

TO BE CONTINUED

THE HOUSE OF HATE

Pearl makes a grisly discovery, while Joe Cuny looks on.

Pearl gestures toward Antonio Moreno, while Joe Cuny (in blackface) is being restrained.

Joe Cuny peeks around the corner to find a startled Pearl and friend.

Masked figures were very popular during the days of the silent serials. "The Hooded Terror" was one of the most sinister of villains. Here he is, doing his worst.

Pearl has just ambushed a villain.

Law and order triumph in the end.

The Dice of Death

"Please fetch Mademoiselle White. I am now ready to rehearse her entrance."

Jacque-Charles directing on the massive stage of the Casino de Paris.

Minutes later Pearl, followed by Margarita, sauntered to center stage, where Jacque-Charles kissed her hand ceremoniously.

"Ah, Mademoiselle, lovely as ever."

"After that all-night party at the Moulin Rouge, I didn't know if I could make it. But there's something about Paris that lets you kick up your heels like no other place in the world, and still punch the timeclock. Now, what's my first skit?"

Jacque-Charles explained enthusiastically, "It isn't exactly a skit. It's more in the mood of your magnificent serials."

Pearl exchanged looks with Margarita as the chorus of boys and girls stared admiringly at her.

The impresario continued gesticulating grandiosely.

"The curtains part revealing a Chinese opium den. A group of oriental ballet dancers, male and female, are performing the dance of the Papaverines. In black silk costumes dotted with huge white, pink, red, orange and purple poppies, intermittently accented by the beating of a gigantic gong hanging center stage, with the orchestra blowing reeds and flutes and plucking strings underneath."

Pearl jumped on a platform at right.

"And I suppose I drift in as queen of the whores smoking a bejewelled opium pipe?"

"No, Mademoiselle. You make your entrance from the balcony."

"From the balcony?"

"Yes, swinging down on a rope; and when you land on stage,

you dance a wild orgy with the transfixed males and as a climax drop into a trap door from which billows of smoke emerge."

The entire company applauded as Jacque-Charles finished bowing. Grabbing both of Pearl's hands, he promised, "Mademoiselle, all Paris will be at your feet."

"And I'll be in the hospital with a broken neck."

"I do not understand."

She lead him to an ornate chair. "Please sit down while I explain a few things: I never did those dangerous stunts like swinging down ropes and jumping off bridges. I had several men who doubled for me."

Clutching his breast and staring blindly at her, the impresario rattled off in French. And then in English. "But I read your life story. You said you were a trapeze artist, a bareback rider in a circus. And all of those things could not be faked. I saw your face close-up."

Pearl lolled on the edge of her chair.

"Jacque-Charles, you know a star must tell fibs—if not for herself then for her public. My early days as an actress were quite dull, going from one tank town to another. I just frilled things for my fans and the newspaper people. They created the Pearl White image—somehow I had to live up to it."

Jumping to his feet, Jacque-Charles bellowed, "But you signed a contract! I have over one million francs invested in this All Star Revue. And you are the biggest star of them all. And what will they see when you appear—Whistler's Mother?"

Pearl stood up. "There is nothing in my contract that says I make an entrance swinging on a rope from the balcony. I read the fine print, Monsieur!"

Pearl stormed off the stage with Margarita at her heels. The stunned producer slouched into his chair as the company whispered.

"Volterra, we are in bad trouble."

Jacque-Charles puffed heavily on his cigar as he stared across the mahogony desk at the director of the Casino de Paris.

"Charles, the only way out, as I see it, is to find out what she can do, and build a new show around her."

"And kill my opium den ballet? Never!" Pounding on the desk. "Without that blonde wig and a half dozen doubles, she is a bitch! She will ruin us. We have staked all on her appearance. If she doesn't at least look like the Cinema Pearl, we are doomed to failure."

Pouring cognac for them both, Volterra raised his glass and said optimistically: "You are France's greatest impresario. I know you will find a way to present Mademoiselle Pearl White without her jumping off the proscenium arch."

"Jacque, you know I've been thinking about what to do in your revue. I'm not much of a singer and never won any contests as a hoofer. Why don't we do a burlesque on some of my serial high-lights?"

Clapping his hands together, Jacque-Charles began to smile broadly.

"That is exactly what I've been thinking about. We will have you make your entrance in this airplane, which will be suspended on wire from the roof of the upper balcony to the stage. It will be completely safe. I once did it with a boy dressed as a swan. And then maybe you can sing a little song."

Pearl shook her head.

"But you just can't stand there and bow."

"If they know I am Pearl White, they'll applaud. And what else can we do?"

The impresario's brow furrowed, he clenched his fists, forcing back another outburst.

In the wings Volterra shook his head, cautioning the impresario to say nothing further.

Later, as she was about to step into the airplane, a bottle fell from the fly, crashing at Pearl's feet. The company was paralyzed with fright; the silence hung like death over the huge empty theatre.

Jacque-Charles swung quickly into action along with Volterra to search the rafters to see who had been up there to cause such a near fatal accident.

"Mademoiselle, would you like to wait for our first rehearsal until tomorrow?"

"No, Jacque, I'm OK. Just a little shaken. Wonder who in hell would be up there tipping a bottle and then letting it almost konk me out."

"We will find out what happened; I give you my word. Now, shall we try the plane ride?"

Pearl and Margarita entered her dressing room. Margarita picked up an envelope from the table.

"Here's something for you, Miss White."

As Pearl slit it open, she commented happily, "You know, M., that plane ride is going to bring down the house."

Reading slowly, she laughed, then re-read it aloud: "Listen to this. 'Mademoiselle White. If you value your life, get out of Paris tonight. The Tongs never forget.' Now, what the hell do you make of that?"

There was a knock on the door, and Leon Volterra pushed it open slowly. "I just came to congratulate you, Mademoiselle, on your plane ride. It will be tremendous."

"I hope so. I just got this."

She handed the note to Volterra, who read it quickly, his face reddening, his eyes bulging, his lips heavy with saliva. "Nom de Dieu! The Tong! The most dreaded gang in the world!"

"But why are they after me?"

"Did you ever offend the Chinese?"

"Well, most of the villains in my serials were Chinese, and in my last it was Warner Oland who played a slant-eyed monster."

"I must call the police. But don't worry. We'll have guards posted everywhere."

He bumped through the door.

Pearl half-smiled. "You know, I'm going to really enjoy this revue. It's just like one of my serials."

Opening night backstage at the Casino de Paris found Jacque-Charles giving last-minute instructions to cast and crew.

"Now, remember, everyone, I want absolute silence until Miss White lands on the stage in the plane. Then uproar and shouts and into the dance of the daredevils."

The stage manager came up.

"Miss White is in the plane, Monsieur."

Jacque-Charles was at center stage.

"Places everyone!"

Dancers hurried to their places as the lights went up.

The Impresario rushed back of the towering airport set. "Let me look at those wires."

Stage hands backed away. Out front, the orchestra blared.

Jacque-Charles, inspecting the wires closely, suddenly gasped:

"Sacre Bleu! Someone has cut the wires! If she comes down now the plane will crash in the audience! What can we do?"

The stage manager thought quickly, "All hands grab those cables to form a human counterweight. Let's hope we can be enough balance."

The stage hands grabbed the cables.

"There's the red light!" Jacque-Charles cried. "Mademoiselle White is descending! Hold onto those cables with your life!"

The orchestra played on. There was an uproar from the audience. Pearl landed on the stage to thunderous applause.

"A most exciting entrance, Mademoiselle," smiled Maurice Chevalier as he kissed Pearl's hand.

"Mademoiselle, it was just like one of your serials, which I adore." chirped Mistinguett, the toast of Paris.

"And Pearl, you knocked 'em dead," said Jack Dempsey.

The dressing room was overflowing with flowers and people.

"Thanks so much, everyone. Won't you join me at Maxime's for a champagne supper Jacque-Charles is paying for?"

Everyone accepted.

"I'll change and meet you all there later."

Slowly the guests and reporters began filing out. Jacque-Charles stayed behind with two police officers. "Mademoiselle White, I do not wish to spoil your premiere night but something happened backstage and I had to call the police. One of the cable wires was cut and only the heroic efforts of the crew saved you from a serious accident."

Pearl turned to Margarita. "Order them a case of the best cognac."

"Mademoiselle White, I am Claude Roget of the Sureté. May I ask you a few questions?"

Pearl lit a cigarette and began removing her makeup.

"Fire away."

"Mademoiselle, do you have any known enemies in Paris?"

"None. As to enemies anywhere, just a couple of ex-husbands who I don't think would want me dead."

"Do you have the note which was supposedly sent by the Tong?"

"No, I thought it was just a joke and threw it away."

"But there have been two attempts on your life, Mademoiselle, and we haven't a single clue."

The room seemed quite stuffy as Pearl finished cleaning her face.

"Our only alternative is to supply you with a police guard at all times. He will take you to and from the theatre and to and from the stage to your dressing room."

"Real cops and robbers, huh?"

"We don't know, but we can not take any further chances after tonight. Thank you, Mademoiselle."

As the Police bowed out Jacque-Charles sighed weakly.

"It seems fate has been against us from the very beginning. Mademoiselle it looks as if we shall take a terrific loss unless something turns up."

"Like what? Me trying to sing like Mistinguett? Jacque, I want to help all I can but, I don't know what to do. I'm new to the stage."

"Will you just try working out a song with our orchestra leader?"

Pearl snuffed out the cigarette. "OK Jacque, I'm really not as much a bitch as you might think."

"My God, Margarita, I don't know how I've gotten through these last ten days! Everytime I sing that damned song I know I sound like a frog. And did you read those reviews? The show is a big flop and they are trying to blame me."

Pearl paced up and down the luxurious apartment as Margarita knitted.

"Miss White, there have been some strange things happening. Maybe it would be best if you just had a talk with Jacque-Charles and Volterra and terminated the contract."

"Maybe that's what they want so they can get out of paying me. No I'm sticking this damned thing out until hell freezes over."

The telephone rang.

"I'll get it. Hello . . . yes, this is Miss White. What? What in heaven's name will happen next? Where's Jacque-Charles and Volterra? . . . I see. Thank you."

She slammed down the receiver: "That was the stage manager. The lousy theatre caught on fire. And guess where? Under the stage where I was going to rehearse this afternoon."

The phone rang again. "Hello, . . . yes. . . . Who is this?"

"MADEMOISELLE WHITE, REMOVE YOURSELF FROM PARIS BEFORE YOU ARE REMOVED. THIS IS YOUR LAST WARNING!"

"Who is this? . . . Hello! Hello!"

She slammed down the receiver again. "Christ almighty! That was some whispering voice warning me to get out of Paris or else."

"Call the police, Miss White!"

"Police! Hell no. I'm calling the steamship lines for a reservation home. This is it!"

TO BE CONTINUED

THE LIGHTNING RAIDER

Pearl was co-starred in this epic with Warner Oland. The Swedish-born actor played the role of a sinister Oriental, Wu Fang, and in the process assumed many disguises. Following are some of them.

In striped pants, Oland assumes a "veddy British" posture.

Oland threatens Pearl. Here he is dressed in conventional garb.

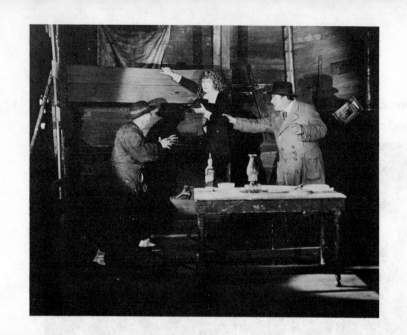

On safari.

As a "mad scientist"?

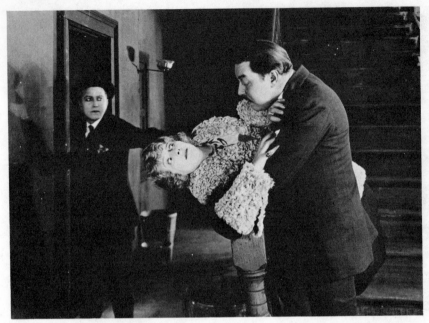

A "great lover"? We doubt if Pearl appreciates his advances.

In Oriental gear.

In Oriental gear.

Pearl subdues the villainous Oland. . . .

He gets away, but it looks as though Pearl has found him again.

William Burt (as "The Wasp") captures Oland . . . for good? Pearl struggles to her feet.

Oland wasn't the only menace in the serial, as Pearl discovers here.

Now Pearl packs a pistol. . . .

The pistol is loaded, but the room seems to be empty.

And here is our heroine with a knife. . . .

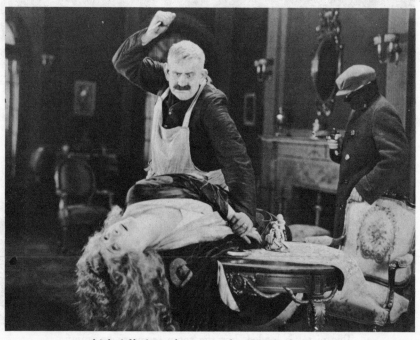

which falls into the wrong hands, we fear. . . .

A struggle ensues.

Pearl is threatened with a blunt instrument.

Pearl visits "scientist" Walter McGrail.

Can that be . . . we're afraid so. Dynamite!

In a more peaceful moment, Pearl rides through darkest Africa, but we're sure things won't stay quiet for long.

Episode Thirteen:

Danger Underground

"M., I've never been so nervous in my life."

"It's just your homecoming," Margarita assured her, helping her into a shimmery white dress.

"Guess you're right—there's nothing like good old American terra firma and the thrill of making another serial."

There was a knock at the door.

"Come in," Pearl called out.

Cuny was poking his head inside the dressing room.

"We're waiting, Pearl." As she stood up and crossed over to him he greeted her, "Pearl, sure glad to have you back. Picture making for Pitch and me ain't been the same without you."

Pecking him on the cheek, she rushed onto the darkened set. Suddenly all lights went up and the entire company headed by director Seitz began singing "For She's a Jolly Good Fellow."

Pearl had tears in her eyes as a big cake reading WELCOME HOME, PEERLESS, FEARLESS GIRL, was rolled out and champagne corks popped.

Pearl and Seitz lit cigarettes as the party simmered down and cameraman Edward Snyder lined up the first shot on *Plunder*.

"Pearl, this Paris frolic sounds like something right out of one of your serials."

"You can say that again." Draining the glass of champagne, Pearl explained, "I don't know whether someone was trying to scare me or murder me. Strange that Jacque-Charles and Volterra were both out of the city when they had the fire at the Casino. And that voice on the phone, it was in the best Prince George the Loud tradition."

"But why, Pearl?" Seitz's eyes were twinkling. "Sure you didn't make the whole thing up so you could collect your salary without breaking your contract?"

Pearl punched him on the shoulder. "A couple of nights I woke up wondering that. But seriously, it was odd the police never came up with a single clue. Maybe it was just a string of coincidences. But enough of Paris, tell me—what have you and Bertram Millhauser dreamed up for *Plunder?*"

Seitz reached for the script. "The action centers around a New York skyscraper under the foundation of which many years ago pirates had buried a chest of priceless jewels, gold doubloons and pieces of eight.

Pearl broke in: "Yo-ho-ho! And a bottle of rum!"

"Come on Pearl, let me finish this or—or, I'll make you walk the plank."

"Shiver my timbers!"

"Well, as I was saying, the villain, discovering the treasure map, tries to obtain controlling stock in the building. You, Pearl, as the leading stockholder, find this out and with the help of a mysterious Mr. Jones, try to out-buy him. And after going through hell for fifteen episodes you triumph."

"Listens like a winner. By the way, what ever happened to my dear frog man Gasnier?"

"He's in Hollywood with Pathé, producing and directing."

Eddie Snyder signalled he was ready for the first scene.

Pearl walked up to the edge of the water tank and smiled at the massive octopus sprawling on the steps leading into the waist-high water.

"Hi, Octi, never thought I'd see you again."

"Hi, Pearl!"

Pearl, startled, stepped back. Suddenly the head opened up and Pitch crawled out grinning.

"How do you like this new model Pearl? I'm the front and Cuny's the rear."

"Lucky me. At last I get between you two guys. Now come over here, and tell me how this damn monster works."

Pitch and Pearl sat on a tentacle.

"Well you know the trouble we had with that one-man octopus."

"Yeah, I almost got drowned. What are the improvements on this model?"

"This one's the genuwine article. It's got eyeballs that I can move every which way. And each of the arms can be worked separately. I work the front ones and Cuny handles the rear. Hell, we even got a built-in inkwell that squirts out that black stuff."

"Oh, I can just feel your slimy embrace."

Seitz waved his cane at them.

"OK, Pearl, let me brief you on the action."

Pitch crawled back into the octopus, followed by Cuny.

Seitz continued. "Your Mr. Jones has fallen through a trap door into the octopus tank. Giant tentacles encircle him. The scene switches back to you, now entering the room above the tank. Searching for Jones, you find the lever, you pull it, the trap opens and down you go; but somehow you manage to grasp the edge, where you dangle. Suddenly, fascinated by your swinging body the octopus uncoils from Jones and as we start to iris out one of its tentacles reaches up and starts to squeeze the life out of you. End of episode."

The studio carpenter's shop rocked with shouts and yells as Pearl rolled seven on the dice.

"I win! I win!"

Pitch threw two dollars on the pile of money in front of Pearl.

"That's the second time you've nosed me out by a length. I think this Frenchy horse game is rigged and the dice are loaded."

"Ah, quit being a poor loser. This is an imported game and it takes time to learn. Remember, you throw the dice and move your little horsey down the track the number of spaces on the board according to the dots on the ivories. Now that isn't too hard is it?"

She picked up the dice and shook them inside her fist: "OK, boys, bets up for the fifth race at Epsom Downs."

A voice came from above.

"OK, Pearl, we're ready for the next scene. Millhauser just finished writing it."

Pearl pocketed her winnings.

"That's what I call getting copy hot off the griddle. Maybe we'd better slow down the action to give him time to knock off the next page."

As the musical trio struck up the exciting "Light Cavalry Overture," Sietz issued instructions:

"OK, let's have that action!"

Pearl burst through the door of the flop house bedroom, followed by the villain.

"That's fine Pearl, now run over to that side table and grab

that bottle. Oettel you make a lunge for her. . . . Fine. Jump up
on the bed Pearl. . . . Now hit him over the head with the bottle!"

Pearl, following Sietz's direction, swung the bottle. The bed
gave a lurch, she lost her footing and fell against the iron bed
railing.

Her agonizing scream brought the entire company rushing
onto the set as Wally Oettel caught her in his arms.

Sietz bent over her.

"Pearl, are you alright? Where's it hurt?"

Clutching her side, she gasped:

"I think I cracked a rib."

The early morning wind ripped across 72nd Street and 3rd
Avenue, as the New York City double-decker bus loaded with
extras waited for Sietz to explain the action.

"Pearl do you feel up to doing a close-up?"

"Sure, George, after these last six weeks, I'll do anything to
break the monotony. But where's that pro stunt guy who's to
double me when I jump from the top of the bus to that elevated
railway?"

"Ah, he hasn't shown up. My chaffeur, Johnny Stevenson, has
been begging me to let him do it. It's an awful dangerous stunt
for an amateur. I don't think I should let him."

"I agree. Just one slip and you know what can happen."

Stevenson approached them.

"Mr. Sietz, I'm all ready. How do I look dressed up like you
Miss White?"

"I think your're much prettier than me." She put her hand on
his shoulder. "But Johnny, I wish you wouldn't do this."

"But I need the money Miss White. Even my wife and daughter are working as extras on the bus."

Sietz and Pearl exchanged frowns.

"OK, Johnny, but remember that's an eighteen-foot drop to
hard pavement."

"Don't worry, Mr. Sietz, I did a lot of tumbling in high
school."

Seitz and Johnny walked over to the man who was driving
the bus.

"Now, Macy, keep the bus exactly at five miles an hour, not a
mile more. This way if Johnny should fall he'll fall back onto
the bus."

"I understand, Mr. Seitz."

"Now, Johnny, you jump on the bus and run to the front as the villains pursue you. Then you rush up on top and as the bus passes under the structure you stand up and grab the girder and climb up out of camera range. We'll take another shot from the railway."

As Seitz stepped behind the camera the wind had a wail in it and black clouds drifted across the eastern sky.

Seitz shouting through his megaphone:

"Lights! Camera! Action!"

Slowly the bus came into camera range and Johnny leaped on, rushing to the top pursued by the villains. He looked back at them and then leaped. But his jump was too high, and hitting his head on the steel girder he fell head down onto the street. His wife's scream tore through the shocked silence.

For a terrifying moment everything stopped. The bus; the camera; the people. And then Seitz yelled: "Call an ambulance!"

Seitz bent over Johnny. "My God, he's dead!"

Pearl rushed up beside him. "What happened?"

"The bus was going too fast, I guess, and Johnny fouled up on his timing."

A young woman and girl slowly walking up to the broken body, stared down as the wind tore at their garments and cried for them. . . .

TO BE CONTINUED

GLAMOR GIRL

In her heyday, Pearl's picture was always in demand. Here are four rare postcards which feature her in various poses.

Against Time

"George, here's a little something to add to the fund for Johnny Stevenson's wife and daughter." Pearl handed him a check. "How is she taking the loss?"

Sietz rolled the glass around in his hands. "Like most of you women—with a smile backed up by a tear."

Pearl finished her drink. "He was so young and so full of life. It's hard to understand."

Sietz put his glass on the black marble-topped coffee table. "You know, Pearl, this sort of thing has never happened to me in all my years directing serials. A human life lost for just a mistake of seconds."

Outside gulls clamored at the winter quiet as the four o'clock sun pulled shadows from the trees and hung them from the windows of the library.

"How about another one, George?"

"No, thanks. I have a long drive back remember."

Pearl half-filled her glass with Scotch, taking a long drink.

As the gulls continued their shrieking the most famous pair in serial picture making seemed drawn apart, isolated in the cold sounds and sights of winter that separated leaf from branch, grass from earth, moans from the low tide waves in the bay below.

Pearl lighting a cigarette moved to the windows and stared down across the browned lawns.

Sietz looked at her as though he hadn't seen her in a long time. Was this the peerless, fearless gal he'd loved for so many years, as friend and star? What was happening to her?

"Winter seems to have set our mood. Where are the happy times, Prince George the Loud? Are they played out?"

He lit a cigarette and continued his thinking. What time had failed to do to Pearl she was doing to herself. He smiled at her, trying to disguise his thoughts. There were wrinkles under the beautiful eyes, and flab under the arms that had thrilled millions as they helped her escape from the grasp of villains. Her fingers were yellow with nicotine, and the sensuous body that had out-done many a man in death-defying stunts was way over-weight.

He stood up, hoping to shake himself loose from his perceptions.

"Pearl," he crossed over to her. "Pathé is sending me out to Hollywood to produce serials with this new girl, Allene Ray. Why don't you come along? They say some day it will be the film capital of the world. It'll be like pioneering all over again."

Pearl watched a newspaper caught up by the wind skittering like a crazy kite and then collapsing into a tree.

"Hollywood? Even the name sounds phoney. No, I've never been there and I don't want to go there."

She was back at the coffee-table emptying her glass, then she turned to face Sietz.

"Now, old pal, *Plunder* is the best serial we ever made. And look—its only playing in second-rate houses and at kiddie matinees. The great days of the to-be-continueds are over. Can Hollywood change that?"

Her voice sounded hollow in the heavily furnished room, echoing an emptiness that hurt all over. She placed her hand about Sietz's shoulder and made up a smile.

"It's not all really over, George. I was about to tell you I've had a rather fabulous offer from Paris, to do features with a serial format: *The Perils of Paris, The Perils of Madrid, The Perils of London.* And I'll be the boss—a second Louie Gasnier."

Sietz chuckled. "Heaven forbid. But I hope it works out for you. But what about that Casino de Paris episode? Maybe some of those 'strange coincidences' are still hanging around."

"You know me better than that. I don't scare off easy. Besides, I met a rather fascinating guy, Ted Cozzika, when I was there— a Greek who's high in financial circles. He's been writing me and asking me to come back. Who knows he may turn out to be my great love and protector."

Laughing she poured another drink. "Maybe this tall, dark and handsome man from the cradle of democracy can free me from all my inhibitions. Maybe even make a weak woman out of me."

The words catching in her throat, she began coughing heavily, and then washed the rasp down with Scotch.

Margarita entered the library.

"Miss White, the real estate agent is here to look over the house."

"You show him around, M."

As she closed the door, Sietz observed, "You really are pulling up stakes."

"Yes, George. What roots have I here? Just dead ones, beginning with McCutcheon." Sipping her drink, she continued, "Last month I visited with sister Grace and my Dad. A sort of reunion. And we had a big surprise—my long lost brother who disappeared years ago was there with his wife. But it wasn't the same. Even the dust seemed to have changed color."

She turned away and brushed a few tears from her eyes.

"You can't go back, George—only forward. Even if it's off a cliff. That's why Paris seems to be a new start for me."

She emptied the glass. "Besides, I'm leaning too much on this stuff. Think I'll spend some time in a convent before I start working. Dry myself out. Pay a little attention to my soul."

Placing both arms around him, she pleaded: "Do I sound like I'm playing little Eva?"

He kissed her gently on the cheek. "You sound like the most wonderful gal I've ever known. If I'd been half a man, and not married to the best wife in the land, I'd have made love to you the first time I saw you."

"You nut!" She kissed him sweetly on the lips. "Remember me, darling, as the woman you never had, but worshipped from behind a camera."

He looked at her for a long moment and then said: "I'm going now, Pearl. Don't see me out. I just want to remember you as you are now. Like in a D. W. Griffith tear-jerker. A slow iris out. . . ."

He bowed stiffly and was gone, his footsteps echoing on the polished floor.

Pearl, back at the window, through a mist of tears watched another wind gust tugging at the newspaper and suddenly setting it free. It tumbled down toward the bay and was carried out to sea by a wave.

TO BE CONTINUED

Is Pearl going to knock that pedestal over at the right moment?

Walter McGrail comes to Pearl's rescue.

Pearl notes with horror that the villain is going to draw a knife. . . .

This time Pearl comes to the aid of McGrail.

McGrail and Pearl express undying love for each other as a new peril awaits them.

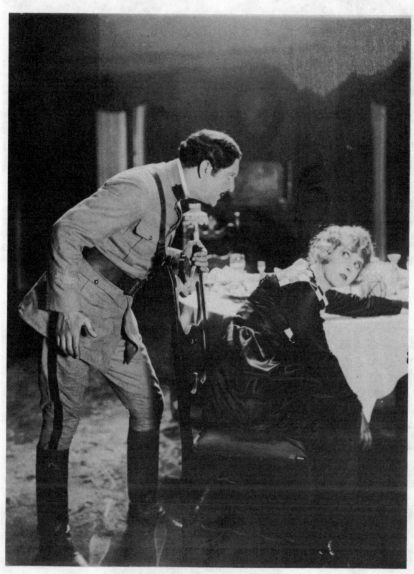

Harry Semels threatens Pearl. . . .

Walter McGrail tries to protect our heroine. . . .

It was like this, officer.

Walter is in trouble again. What's Pearl going to do?

The action moves outdoors.

Pearl seems reluctant to help the gentleman experiencing breathing difficulties.

Pearl's not exactly Juliet, but then Walter McGrail isn't wooing her here.

A chair and a pointed finger wouldn't appear to be much of a match for that rifle.

Pearl and Walter McGrail take time out to talk things over.

Pearl is in danger again.

Pearl and Walter are surprised by the gentleman at the window.

Everybody has a pistol in this scene. It doesn't look as though the two guys on the left know that Pearl and Walter are there.

Pearl seems to be the only one sober here.

Pearl "says cheese."

The whiteness of Pearl makes a good contrast with the blackness of the villain.

As usual, Walter McGrail comes to Pearl's aid.

Wally McCutcheon threatens Pearl and Walter....

But good triumphs over evil....

Wally is "all tied up."

Pearl encounters some difficulties with the military.

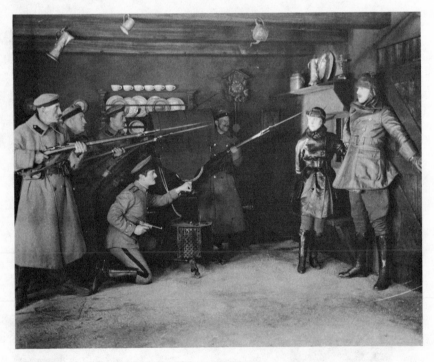

A cave-in.

Is Pearl stranded in the jungle again?

An evil-doer is disarmed. . . .

But first they had to capture him.

Flowers for our heroine.

Pearl never *did* get to knock over that pedestal. But a gun's a better weapon anyhow.

A Woman's Perfidy

"Miss White," Margarita said, "here is Miss Norris of the *Motion Picture Classic Magazine* for the interview."

"Pleased to meet you Miss Norris, make yourself comfortable. Oh Margarita, please fetch us some cognac."

The youthful Miss Norris raised an eyebrow as Pearl lit a small cigar.

"Care for one, my dear? I have them made specially in Havana."

"No, thank you, but I'll take a cigarette if you have one."

As Pearl handed her a gold case, she blew a large smoke ring.

Miss Norris, lighting a cigarette, leaned back against the pink satin divan and thought: Could this be the harum-scarum star of more than a decade ago? When her wild perils were as popular as apple pie and bow-tied shoes. Resplendent in a sky-blue tulle frock with Rue de la Paix written all over it, she looked more a model from Paris than a gal from Missouri who had raised the pulse of the world flying on girders and jumping off bridges.

"Miss Norris, you mean your magazine sent you all the way from America to interview me?"

Miss Norris opened her purse and took out a writing pad and pencil as Margarita poured the cognac.

"America," Pearl continued, "it seems so far away. Hmmm, America—the home of the dry and the land of the free."

Miss Norris smiled. "I'll drink to that."

Both ladies tipped glasses.

"You mean they still remember me back home?"

"Of course they remember you. You are an immortal of the silver screen. But tell me, why haven't you made any more French movies since *The Perils of Paris?*"

"My producer had King Alfonso of Spain interested in backing the next film, *The Perils of Madrid*. For some unknown reason he backed out. Later my producer wanted to do one on London, but I didn't like his new format. So now I'm just racing my stable of horses, enjoying the social whirl and reading any new scripts that are sent to me."

"Will you ever make another film in America?"

"I don't know. With this Talkie craze, who knows what will happen to pictures?"

"Will you ever come back to the States to live?"

Pearl sipped her cognac.

"I've made several trips back. But there's something about Paris that gets you body and soul. A French proverb reads, 'everyone in the world has two countries—his own and France.'"

The ladies listened to the rising rush of late afternoon traffic on the Avenue Henri Martin, as Margarita slowly drew the heavy drapes.

"Miss White, the gossip columnists are predicting that you and Mr. Cozzika will soon be married."

"Well, we have just returned from a world tour, but I can assure you, it wasn't a honeymoon." Pearl ground her cigar into a Mexican onyx ashtray.

"Well, what's the story about you and Mr. Cozzika running a gambling casino?"

"Yes, I acquired the old Hotel de Paris in Biarritz, once the chateau of the Empress Eugenie. I turned the drawing room into the casino, and I've kept the imperial boudoir for my private apartment."

Pearl went on sipping her cognac. "And have you heard the latest rumor?"

Miss Norris bit her pencil. "No; is this an exclusive?"

"You can call it that, if you like." Pearl rubbed a large ruby ring on her left hand.

"Well, the latest rumor is, that Mr. Cozzika and I are running a whore house!"

Miss Norris, putting her pad and pencil into her purse, finished her cognac, and smiled at her hostess.

As the telephone rang, Pearl stood up. "Any further questions, Miss Norris?"

The young lady stood up.

"No, Miss White. This has been a most illuminating interview. I am sure all of your fans will adore it."

Margarita opened the door.

As Miss Norris disappeared down the walk into the Chateau garden, Pearl yelled: "That dirty little slut digging into my private life!"

Picking up the phone she snapped, "Who the hell is this?"

TO BE CONTINUED

PLUNDER

Pearl in the middle of a barroom brawl.

Wally Oettel picks up Pearl. . . .

She gets away, but Wally recaptures her on the staircase. . . .

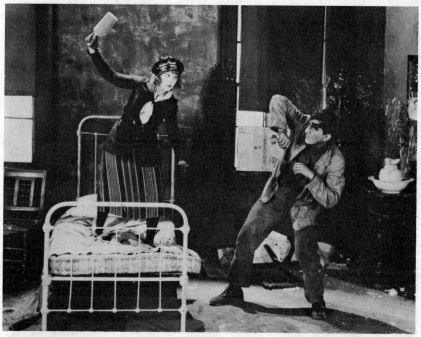

Pearl reaches her room where she cows Wally with a bottle. (The Peerless Fearless Girl broke a rib in this scene.)

Pearl on the rocks.

"Pirate" Pearl poses for publicity shot. (The John Robyns Collection)

A brief moment of rest.

In the "Swamp of Lost Souls" episode, Pearl finds herself in the soup with
Warren William. . . .

and some of the locals.

Pearl in trouble again. . . .

Back to the swamp.

Captured again. . . .

. . . and again.

The villains try to extract some information from Pearl.

Pearl interrupts a conversation. . . .

A chase ensues. . . .

Finally a battering ram is brought into play.

At last! The treasure! (Harry Semels is the lucky guy.)

Surveying the wreckage. . . .

Subduing an attacker. . . .

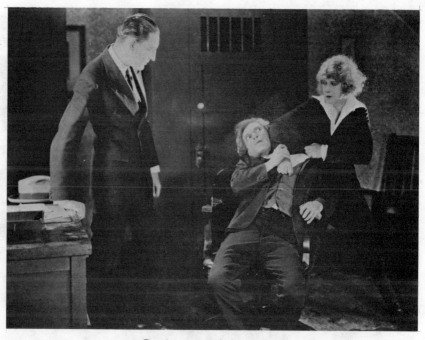

Getting some information.

The redskin tells Harry Semels what Pearl's been up to.

In a dream sequence, Pearl journeys back to the middle ages. Harry Semels is at the left.

Pearl looks as though she's glad *that's* over. (The John Robyns Collection)

The Reckoning

"Miss White, I don't believe you realize how serious your condition is."

Pearl lay in the white-satin-covered bed like a statue.

"You have a mild jaundice and an increasing dropsy. These are activated by your over-eating, drinking and lack of rest."

The big eyes opened slowly, staring at the young man sitting beside the massive bed: Dr. Edmund L. Gros, Doctor. There had not been many doctors in her life. Now he was the most important. Was he frightening her? Was she as bad as all that? Some days she felt so. Maybe this was just one of those days. The beginning of the end. THE END—how many serials had faded out on those two words? How far was the final fade-out everyone must face? Wasn't this the day Cozzika was returning from Greece? What day was it?

Feeling her pulse the doctor said: "If you don't be a good girl and obey me, I'll have to put you in the hospital."

Pearl sat up. "I've never been in a hospital in my life, Doctor."

"But we must have tests, and you must be relaxed and get away from all this pressure and night-clubbing."

Margarita pulled pillows around to support her back.

"Doctor, I'm pushing fifty. I've lived a pressure-life. It's the only way I know. My old studio, Pathé, advertised me as the Peerless, Fearless Girl. And an actress must always live up to her publicity." She forced a smile as he dropped her hand.

"It's your life, Miss White. I'm sure you'll live it as you want without heeding my advice. But just remember I warned you as your doctor and—I hope—your friend."

The doctor rose and Pearl reached for his hand.

"I appreciate your trying to help. And I have tried to stop the boozing and eating. I have tried. But somehow I last just a few days——"

She let his hand slip from hers and tears filled her eyes.

"Margarita, have this prescription filled for Miss White. And Miss White, please rest at least today and tonight. I'll look in on you tomorrow."

The telephone beside the bed rang. As Pearl picked up the receiver she said to the doctor, now at the door: "I'll be OK, Doctor. Have patience with me." As he left the palatial bedroom, she said hello into the telephone.

"Yes. This is she. . . Ted? I didn't recognize your voice. Must be a bad connection. So you are back? Wonderful, wonderful. When will I see you? . . . Fine . . . No, I'm just lolling in bed. Too many parties. See you around three . . . Goodbye, darling. Just hearing you does more for me than all those shots Doctor Gros punches in my fanny."

"That was Ted," Pearl explained to Margarita, who was returning with a breakfast tray. "At long last he's back. Maybe his mother has agreed to our marriage."

Margarita was about to place the tray on the bed.

"No, M. I'm too excited for breakfast. Just a piece of toast and a small brandy. And prepare my henna bath. Tonight Ted is taking me to the most famous party giver in Europe. The Italian Countess Maia Majesta, who is celebrating her eightieth birthday."

Margarita hesitated. "But Miss White, didn't you listen to what the doctor said? Rest—no parties and no drinking. Please, Miss White, I'm worried about you. I've never seen you like this before."

Pearl, in a pink chiffon nightgown, slipped out of bed.

"You too? My faithful M.—friend, confidante, right arm."

She motioned for her to sit on the bed. "M., I've lived one pattern all my life. I can't change now. I've never been so happy as with Cozzika. And there are times I've never been so sad. Nobody can change me but me. I'll face the music whatever the tune."

Pearl kissed her on the cheek. There were tears in Margarita's eyes. Suddenly she embraced Pearl, crying softly on her shoulder. A sparrow pecked at the window and the bells of Notre Dame chimed the Angelus . . .

The yellow Rolls Royce swung off the main road and stopped before a tall iron gate. A guard, dressed as a seventeenth-century French soldier, stepped briskly forward, and after checking the gold embossed invitation Cozzika had handed the chauffeur, opened the gates and motioned the car forward. Cozzika leaned back against the leopard-skin seat and turned to Pearl as the car pulled behind a long line of limousines and moved slowly up the driveway leading to the towering castle on the hill.

"You see, darling, the Countess was born on Mayday and all her parties are fashioned around the great Pagan festivals that began with the Romans."

Pearl asked: "Didn't the Maypole come from their Festival of flowers?"

"Correct. And in most instances quite phallic."

Pearl giggled and fluffed her dress of peacock feathers. "Well, I'll try anything once."

Cozzika kissed her passionately. "It's marvelous being with you again, darling. I've missed you so much."

Pearl smiled. "I've missed you. By the way, Ted, what did your mother say about our proposed marriage?"

Cozzika frowned. "She didn't say anything." Holding her tightly in his arms, he continued, "But tradition or not, nobody can ever separate us!"

He kissed her again as the car came to a stop before a rise of stairs that swept halfway across the entrance to the grey stone castle. The chauffeur opened the door, and Pearl giggled again and said: "Be sure I don't try that Maypole without a couple of absinthes in me."

More seventeenth-century soldiers lined the way, and as massive wooden doors parted, a sprawling marble-floored hall led to a gigantic flight of stairs circling up and out of sight. At the right a line leading to the ballroom was forming. Here the Countess Maia Majesta stood, flanked by two seven-year-old, half-naked Negro boys decked in garlands and bells that tinkled at their slightest movement. Her greeting was a smile that a mummy would have been proud of. A small, shrivelled woman with wrinkles and all that age courts, she dominated the entire scene. All the glitter, from chandeliers to diamond tiaras and the gentle Viennese waltz drifting from the bandstand, waited on her every gesture and word. She wore a transparent white flowing gown familiar to those honored by the vestal virgins. She spoke at least a dozen languages. She said to Pearl: "Miss White, how nice of you to come. I've seen all your films and wondered how one so beautiful could risk her life in so many frightening ways."

Pearl smiled back. "It is a great pleasure to meet you, Count-

ess. I have never seen anything like this even in a Cecil B. De-
Mille epic."

The Countess laughed and reached for a tiny jewelled goblet
one of her small attendants was holding up. "One gets thirsty
speaking to so many friends."

As Cozzika bowed and kissed her wrinkled hand, the Countess
turned her attention to him: "Charming to see you again, Cozzika. And Miss White is all you said and more. Now enjoy your-
selves while I welcome my other guests."

As they walked into the ballroom a seven-foot man wearing
gladiator garb stepped up to Pearl and Cozzika. He was carrying
a tray of drinks in silver chalices.

"Mademoiselle, Monsieur, would you care for a Bona Dea?"

"And to whom is this drink in honor?"

The Gladiator, bowing, continued: "Bona Dea is known as
the good goddess worshipped by women for her chastity and fer-
tility. The Countess has had five of the most famous mixologists
in the world create this tribute to Bona Dea."

As Pearl reached for a chalice, "Monsieur Gladiator, how do
you drink this?"

"Mademoiselle, if you look closely underneath the orchids and
mandarin oranges, you'll find a tiny silver straw. Just sip and
dream."

A voice reaching out through the halls invited the guests into
the third ballroom, where the dance to Fauna would be performed
around the Maypole.

In the center of this ballroom a great pole decorated with
thousands of vari-colored balloons reached to the ceiling. From
the pole hundreds of red, blue, green and yellow streamers hung
to the floor.

Pearl and Cozzika followed the merry crowd that pushed in
from all sides.

From a balcony the orchestra, clad in Roman togas, plucked
out a gay tune on stringed instruments.

The lights changed to rainbow colors as dozens of ten-year-old
boys and girls, dressed as fauns rushed in. Each grabbed a
streamer and began the dance.

As a whirlpool widened, the dancing figures reached the on-
lookers.

Shouting and laughing they extended their hands for an adult
partner.

In a few moments the floor was filled with frolicking dancers.

Pearl was the wildest as she followed the circle of figures around the pole.

Hands on a long streamer, she threw back her head, laughing gayly as two little boys trotted wildly around her.

At the peak of the dance thousands of balloons floated down from the ceiling, their bursts mingling with the shrieks and laughter of the guests.

Another voice announced that dinner was served.

Pearl and Cozzika walked beside a heart-shaped pool surrounded by high walls.

"Ted, these Bona Deas are getting to me. I feel dizzy as hell."

"Pearl, you're teasing. The party has just begun. At midnight the old gal will appear to let loose the vestal virgins and the orgy really begins."

Pearl swayed away from him.

"What the hell do I want a vestal virgin for?"

"Pearl, what's wrong?"

She stared down at her shimmering face in the pool and suddenly threw up. "God, I'm sick as hell! Please let me alone. I don't even want you to see me like this."

He waited and then disappeared into the shadows.

Pearl lay down beside the pool, washing her face. The cool water was soothing to her throbbing temples. Turning on her back she watched the moon through the trees. And then stared up as the figure of the Countess Maia Majesta stood over her. "Mademoiselle, I see my party has upset you. I'm sorry."

Pearl struggled to her feet, brushed at the wet peacock feathers around her neck. "Oh, Countess, I'm so ashamed. This has never happened to me before. Please accept my apologies."

Pearl could feel the Countess's perfumed breath on her cheek.

"Mademoiselle, I see you are under great emotional stress. I know Cozzika. I know his family. I am trying to know you. This is a festival time—a cleaning time or a fatal time. Who knows? Surely not me at eighty. But may I suggest a ritual that has always revived me?"

Pearl brushed at her damp hair, the face of the Countess slowly coming into focus.

"What do you mean?"

A clawed hand touched her shoulder.

"A woman reaches an age when it's life or death. This can be either mental or physical. I feel this is what is happening to you. And if you will follow me across to the meadow, I will show you what I mean."

Pearl stumbled after the old woman who seemed to float across the grass.

A long meadow dipped away from the rocks and trees and on it the moon had laid a silver carpet.

"Maia, whom I am named after, was the eldest of the Pleiades, the seven daughters of Atlas and Pleione the Oceanid. And her magic was famous throughout the world. But her most potent was nature's own—the evening dew of Mayday. Faces, bodies, and souls that washed in it were cleansed of all evil."

Pearl was hypnotized by the droning voice. "Mademoiselle, the meadow waits for you, and the violets are overflowing with dew."

Pearl stared at the meadow, stared at the silver carpet wavering like a wave. Suddenly she ran toward it and flung herself face down.

Across the meadow the voice of the Countess was chanting an ancient ritual, as the silver carpet was turned black by a cloud defacing the moon . . .

TO BE CONTINUED

FEATURE FILMS

BEYOND PRICE
Pearl displays a negligee she designed herself.

A murder is discovered.

BROADWAY PEACOCK

A "just between us girls" scene.

Pearl proposes a toast.

A boudoir scene.

Pearl shows off her wardrobe.

Pearl shows off her plumage.

Pearl makes an unusual entrance.

Bruce McRae and William Riley Hatch are featured in this display of weapons.

Is Pearl handing over a gun, or is she preventing its use?

KNOW YOUR MAN

Pearl is present at the discovery of an important document.

Pearl plays a love scene in picturesque surroundings.

THE MOUNTAIN WOMAN

Pearl plays a Western scene.

Robert Lee strikes a dramatic pose . . . but it looks as though he's only getting ready to brush his teeth.

Robert Lee seems ready to fight for Pearl.

Robert and Pearl talks things over.

Pearl is present at an accusation.

Here, our heroine is being asked to keep her voice down.

There seems to have been trouble on the staircase.

More accusations.

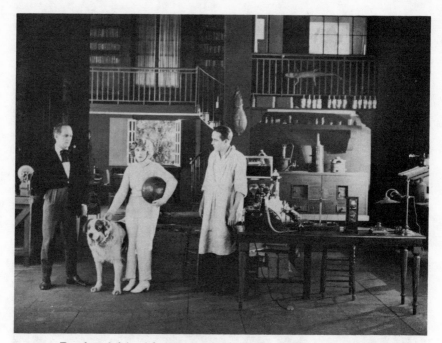

Pearl and friend have come back from a workout in the gym.

Pearl strikes a terrified pose as trouble develops.

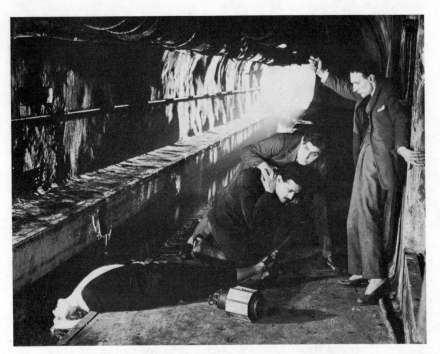

Will the fight end before Pearl's head sinks under the water?

Is it a bird? A plane? Well something in the air is bringing trouble!

Pearl was famous for her dramatic escapes.

The chap with the monocle should be happy at the card his partner has played . . . or did he play the Ace?

A chemical potion is given the once-over.

Pearl chats with Robert Lee and friend.

THE THIEF

All eyes seem to be on Pearl.

Pearl plays a winter scene.

As Pearl encounters difficulties with one bad guy, the other one takes away her baby.

A sled is brought into the action.

Pearl poses with brave Husky, who is going to pull the sled.

A struggle breaks out, but Pearl is hanging onto the baby this time.

Sadism *c.* 1920.

You'd think Pearl was telling a fish story the way she's gesturing.

THE WHITE MOLL

Pearl is threatening instead of being threatened for a change.

An animated discussion is taking place concerning the jewelry.

Pearl helps to divide up the loot.

End of the Trail

Time had no clock as Margarita waited outside Pearl's private room in the American Hospital at Neuilly. Time just waited too.

"Miss Margarita, don't you think you should get some rest? It's past midnight. You've been here for hours."

She looked up at the nurse and tried to smile.

"As long as Miss White is ill in that room, I must wait here. She may want to speak to me. She may want something only I can give her."

She blinked away a tear.

"You see, Miss, she's like my own flesh and blood."

The nurse smiled and moved down the white hallway.

Margarita rubbed at a pain in her neck and leaning her head against the white wall thought: Was this truly the end? Had all the crowded, exciting years come to a stop in that tight white room with her looking so lost in the white sheets? And with Father Theodore Neslay giving her the Last Rites?

Slowly the door opened and the Catholic priest stood beside her. Margarita rose quickly from the bench.

"How is she, Father?"

"She was comatose for a while and then opened her eyes as I began my prayers, and I believe understood me. She even pressed my hand when I anointed her with the Holy oils. She is at peace, I am sure. The rest is up to Almighty God now."

"I hope she isn't suffering."

"The doctor assured me she felt no pain."

"Thank you, Father, for coming. I know this is what she wanted."

"She's a fine woman, Margarita. It was the least I could do after her building a church for me on her Rambouillet estate. We must know our Lord will be merciful."

The priest's footsteps echoed down the hall.

Margarita listened for more sounds. She heard only her own heartbeat, and suddenly she was dozing off.

"Margarita, Margarita, wake up!"

Cozzika shook her gently.

"Oh, Mr. Cozzika! Why are you here?"

"The hospital called me. Pearl is sinking fast."

Margarita, burying her head against his shoulder, sobbed softly.

He lifted her chin and wiped her tears away with his handkerchief. "Now, let's go in."

Two nurses and the doctor were at the bedside. Cozzika and Margarita stared at the gaunt face smothered in whiteness. The eyes were closed.

The only movement was the labored breathing. It struggled to part the lips. It tattered the quiet like a tear in a woolen blanket. Soon it filled the room. And everyone waited on each gasp.

As the doctor reached for the pulse a handful of petals from the vase of white roses on the nightstand fell to the floor.

The breathing hesitated, then strained, then stopped . . .

The doctor looked at his watch. It was 1:50 A.M., August 4, 1938, and Pearl White was dead, like the white petals that lay on the floor beside her body . . .

THE END

Pearl White at 15; her first professional photo.

Pearl at 18.

Pearl in a bathing suit pose.

Pearl in 1910—two poses

Publicity still for the Pathé company, 1911.

Pearl as she appeared in 1914.

Pearl poses as Gainsborough's *Duchess of Devonshire*, 1920. (Photo by Alfred Cheney Johnston.)

Pearl as St. Joan. (Photo by Alfred Cheney Johnston.)

Undated photo of **Pearl**.

Undated photo of Pearl in alluring pose.

Pearl combs her famous wig for the camera.

Two undated closeups of Pearl.

(Photo courtesy *Cinemathèque Française*)

Pearl poses as aviatrix, *c.* 1922.

Pearl as she appeared returning from Paris in 1937.

The Films of Pearl White

POWERS FILM COMPANY

241 Street,
New York, N.Y.

As in the early days of films, credits were not given, this is an incomplete list.
THE MISSING BRIDEGROOM, July 26, 1910
THE NEW MADALENE, November 19, 1910
THE WOMAN HATER, November 26, 1910—With Stuart Holmes
WHEN THE WORLD SLEEPS, December 3, 1910
THE COUNT OF MONTE CRISTO, January 14, 1911

LUBIN FILM COMPANY

Philadelphia, Pa.

Incomplete list.
HELPING HIM OUT, April 20, 1911

PATHÉ FILM COMPANY

1 Congress Street
Jersey City, N.J.

Incomplete list.
MEMORIES OF THE PAST, August 20, 1911
THROUGH THE WINDOW, August 23, 1911—With Octavia Handworth
THE POWER OF LOVE, November (?), 1911—With Crane Wilbur
THE LOST NECKLACE, November 25, 1911—With Octavia Handworth and Roy Smith
THE ARROW-MAKER'S DAUGHTER, August 7, 1912—With Paul Panzer

These films released after Pearl White left Pathé.
PALS, November 9, 1913
DAISY WINS THE DAY, November 9, 1913
AT THE BURGLAR'S COMMAND, November 11, 1913
THE LASS THAT LOVED A SAILOR, (No date)—With Paul
Panzer

CRYSTAL FILM COMPANY

430 Claremont Parkway
New York, N.Y.

The following cast worked with Pearl White in most of her Crystal films:
Chester Barnett (Leading man)
Harry Gsell
Joseph T. Belmont
David Davis
Edwin Hickok
Geraldine McCann
Kathryn Dana
Miriam Collins
Margarite Wolff
Blanche Syres

THE GIRL IN THE ROOM, October 6, 1912 (First film)
THE DRESSMAKER'S BILLS, October 13, 1912
BELLA'S BEAUS, October 20, 1912
A PAIR OF FOOLS, October 27, 1912
OH, SUCH A NIGHT, November 3, 1912
THE GYPSY FLIRT, November 10, 1912
THE CHORUS GIRL, November 17, 1912
LOCKED OUT, December 1, 1912
A TANGLED MARRIAGE, December 8, 1912
THE MIND CURE, December 15, 1912
HIS WIFE'S STRATAGEM, December 22, 1912
HER VISITOR, December 29, 1912
HER KID SISTER, January 5, 1913
HEROIC HAROLD, January 12, 1913
A DIP INTO SOCIETY, January 19, 1913
PEARL'S ADMIRERS, January 26, 1913
WITH HER RIVAL'S HELP, February 2, 1913
ACCIDENT INSURANCE, February 9, 1913
STRICTLY BUSINESS, February 16, 1913
THAT OTHER GIRL, February 23, 1913
A NIGHT IN TOWN, March 2, 1913
KNIGHTS AND LADIES, March 9, 1913
LOVERS THREE, March 23, 1913
THE DRUMMER'S NOTE BOOK, March 30, 1913
PEARL AS A CLAIRVOYANT, April 6, 1913
THE VEILED LADY, April 13, 1913

TWO LUNATICS, April 20, 1913
FORGETFUL FLOSSIE, April 27, 1913
PEARL AS A DETECTIVE, May 4, 1913
WHEN LOVE IS YOUNG, May 11, 1913
HOMLOCK SHERMES, May 18, 1913
TOODLEUMS, May 25, 1913
MARY'S ROMANCE, June 3, 1913
THE NEW TYPIST, June 8, 1913
A CALL FROM HOME, June 17, 1913
WILL POWER, June 22, 1913
AN HOUR OF TERROR, July 1, 1913
THE GIRL REPORTER, July 6, 1913
PEARL'S DILEMMA, July 13, 1913
THE HALLROOM GIRLS, July 20, 1913
THE BROKEN SPELL, July 22, 1913
THE PAPER DOLL, July 29, 1913
WHO IS IN THE BOX?, July 29, 1913
WHAT PAPA GOT, August 3, 1913
A CHILD'S INFLUENCE, August 5, 1913
OH! YOU SCOTCH LASSIE, August 10, 1913
PEARL AND THE TRAMP, August 17, 1913
CAUGHT IN THE ACT, August 19, 1913
A GREATER INFLUENCE, August 19, 1913
MUCH ADO ABOUT NOTHING, September 2, 1913
LOST IN THE NIGHT, September 7, 1913
PLEASING HER HUSBAND, September 9, 1913
THE HAND OF PROVIDENCE, September 14, 1913
A NEWS ITEM, September 16, 1913
MISPLACED LOVE, September 21, 1913
PEARL AND THE POET, September 23, 1913
HIS LAST GAMBLE, September 28, 1913
DRESS REFORM, October 7, 1913
THE WOMAN AND THE LAW, October 12, 1913
PEARL'S MISTAKE, October 14, 1913
HEARTS ENTANGLED, October 19, 1913
WILLIE'S GREAT SCHEME, October 21, 1913
ROBERT'S LESSON, October 26, 1913
HIS RICH UNCLE, October 28, 1913
A HIDDEN LOVE, November 2, 1913
GIRLS WILL BE BOYS, November 4, 1913
WHEN DUTY CALLS, November 9, 1913
O! YOU PEARL, November 11, 1913
OUT OF THE GRAVE, November 16, 1913
HER SECRETARIES, November 18, 1913
THE CABARET SINGER, November 23, 1913
HUBBY'S NEW COAT, November 25, 1913
THE CONVICT'S DAUGHTER, November 30, 1913
A WOMAN'S REVENGE, December 7, 1913
PEARL'S HERO, December 9, 1913

FIRST LOVE, December 14, 1913
THE SOUBRETTE, December 16, 1913
THE HEART OF AN ARTIST, December 21, 1913
LURE OF THE STAGE, December 28, 1913
THE KITCHEN MECHANIC, December 30, 1913
THE LIFTED VEIL, January 4, 1914
SHADOWED, January 6, 1914
THE RING, January 11, 1914
IT MAY COME TO THIS, January 13, 1914
A FATHER'S DEVOTION, January 18, 1914
THE SHADOW OF CRIME, January 25, 1914
OH! YOU PUPPY, January 27, 1914
A GRATEFUL OUTCAST, February 1, 1914
WHAT DIDN'T HAPPEN TO MARY, February 3, 1914
FOR A WOMAN, February 8, 1914
GETTING RUEBEN BACK, February 10, 1914
A SURE CURE, February 15, 1914
LIZZIE AND THE ICE MAN, March 8, 1914
GOING SOME, March 31, 1914
THE LADY DOCTOR, April 5, 1914
GET OUT AND GET UNDER, April 7, 1914
A TELEPHONE ENGAGEMENT, May 5, 1914
THE DANCING CRAZE, May 19, 1914
EASY MONEY, June 2, 1914
HER NEW HAT, June 30, 1914
WHAT PEARL'S PEARLS DID, July 14, 1914
WILLIE'S DISGUISE, August 11, 1914
EAST LYNN IN BUGVILLE, September 22, 1914
SOME COLLECTORS, October 13, 1914
OH! YOU MUMMY, November 17, 1914

The following Pearl White Crystal films were advertised, but no release date available.

PEARL AND THE BURGLARS
PEARL'S ADVENTURE
PEARL'S ROMANCE
THE BUNC THAT FAILED
COPS IS BUSINESS
THE MANIAC'S DESIRE
A LADY IN DISTRESS
THE BOOK AGENTS
THE TELL TALE BLOTTER
OUT OF THE PAST
WHEN LOVE WAS YOUNG
WHO'S THE GOAT?

Unable to trace the source of this Pearl White film. But believed to be Crystal.

MAD LOVER

PATHÉ FILM COMPANY

1 Congress Street
Jersey City, N.J.

THE PERILS OF PAULINE, March 31, 1914—December 12, 1914
Producers: Leopold and Theodore Wharton
Directors: Louis Gasnier, Donald Mackenzie
Scenario: Charles W. Goddard
Cast: Crane Wilbur, Paul Panzer, Edward Jose, Francis Carlyle, Eleanor
    Woodruff, Donald Mackenzie, Clifford Bruce, Sam Ryan, Jack Stand-
    ing, Louis Gasnier, Joe Cuny, Charles (Pitch) Revada, Frank Red-
    man Sr.
Chapter Titles: None
20 episodes.

THE EXPLOITS OF ELAINE, December 28, 1914—August 30, 1915
Producers: Leopold and Theodore Wharton
Directors: Louis Gasnier, George B. Seitz
Scenario: Charles W. Goddard, George B. Seitz, from stories by Arthur B.
    Reeve
Cast: Creighton Hale, Arnold Daly, Sheldon Lewis, Floyd Buckley, Edwin
    Arden, Ramon Owens, Lee Roy Barker, Bessie Wharton
Chapter Titles:
    1. The Clutching Hand
    2. The Twilight Sleep
    3. The Vanishing Jewels
    4. The Frozen Safe
    5. The Poisoned Room
    6. The Vampire
    7. The Double Trap
    8. The Hidden Voice
    9. The Death Ray
    10. The Life Current
    11. The Hour of Three
    12. The Blood Crystals
    13. The Devil Worshippers
    14. The Reckoning
This serial was released in Europe under the title "The Mysteries of
New York." But is popularly remembered as: "The Clutching Hand."

THE NEW EXPLOITS OF ELAINE, April 5, 1915
Producers: Leopold and Theodore Wharton
Director: George B. Seitz
Scenario: Charles W. Goddard and George B. Seitz from stories by Arthur
    B. Reeve
Cast: Creighton Hale, Arnold Daly, Edwin Arden, M. W. Rale
Chapter Titles:
    1. The Serpent Sign
    2. The Cryptic Ring

3. The Watching Eye
4. The Vengeance of Wu Fang
5. The Saving Circles
6. Spontaneous Combustion
7. The Ear in the Wall
8. The Opium Smugglers
9. The Tell-Tale Heart
10. Shadows of War

THE ROMANCE OF ELAINE, June 14, 1915

Producers: Leopold and Theodore Wharton
Director: George B. Seitz
Scenario: Charles W. Goddard and George B. Seitz, from stories by Arthur
     B. Reeve
Cast: Creighton Hale, Arnold Daly, Lionel Barrymore
Chapter Titles:
1. The Lost Torpedo
2. The Gray Friar
3. The Vanishing Man
4. The Submarine Harbor
5. The Conspirators
6. The Wireless Detective
7. The Death Cloud
8. The Searchlight Gun
9. The Life Chain
10. The Flash
11. The Disappearing Helmet
12. The Triumph of Elaine

THE KING'S GAME, January 7, 1916

Producer: Arnold Daly
Adapted from the play of the same title by George B. Seitz
Cast: George Probert, Sheldon Lewis, Nora Moore, George Parks

HAZEL KIRKE, January 28, 1916

Adapted by Steele Mackaye from a play of the same title
Cast: William Riley Hatch, Bruce McRae, Allen Murnane, Creighton Hale,
     Florence Edney

THE IRON CLAW, February 28, 1916—July 10, 1916

Producers: Leopold and Theodore Wharton
Director: Edward Jose, George B. Seitz
Scenario: George B. Seitz from a story by Arthur Stringer
Cast: Creighton Hale, Sheldon Lewis, Harry Fraser, J. E. Dunn, E. Cooper
     Willis, Carey Lee, Allan Walker, (Mrs.) Clare Miller
Chapter Titles:
1. The Vengeance of Legar
2. The House of Unhappiness
3. The Cognac Cask

4. The Name and the Game
5. The Intervention of Tito
6. The Spotted Warning
7. The Hooded Helper
8. The Ghost Man
9. Arrows of Hate
10. The Living Dead
11. The Saving of Dan O'Mara
12. The Haunted Canvas
13. The Hidden Face
14. The Plunge for Life
15. The Double Resurrection
16. The Unmasking of Davy
17. The Vanishing Fakir
18. The Green-Eyed God
19. The Cave of Despair
20. The Triumph of The Laughing Mask

PEARL OF THE ARMY, December 3, 1916—March 11, 1917
Director: Edward Jose
Scenario: G. W. McConnell and George B. Seitz
Cast: Ralph Kellard, Theodore Friebus, Joe Cuny, Marie Wayne, Floyd
    Buckley, W. T. Carleton
Chapter Titles:
1. The Traitor
2. Found Guilty
3. The Silent Menace
4. War Clouds
5. Somewhere in Grenada
6. Major Brent's Perfidy
7. For the Stars and Stripes
8. International Diplomacy
9. The Monroe Doctrine
10. The Silent Army
11. A Million Volunteers
12. The Foreign Alliance
13. Modern Buccaneers
14. The Flag Despoiler
15. The Colonel's Orderly

MAYBLOSSOM, April 8, 1917
Producer: Astra
Director: Edward Jose
Cast: Niles Welch, Hal Ford, Fuller Mellish
Released in Europe under the title: "Annabelle's Romance."

THE FATAL RING, July 8, 1917–November 18, 1917
Director: George B. Seitz
Scenario: Bertram Millhauser from a story by Fred Jackson

Cast: Earle Fox, Warner Oland, Ruby Hoffman, Harry Gsell, Floyd
Buckley, Caesare Gravina, Mattie Ferguson, Richard LaMarr, Mrs.
Spencer Bennet

Chapter Titles:

1. The Violet Diamond
2. The Crushing Wall
3. Borrowed Identity
4. The Warning on the Ring
5. Danger Underground
6. Rays of Death
7. The Signal Lantern
8. The Switch in the Safe
9. The Dice of Death
10. The Perilous Plunge
11. The Short Circuit
12. The Desperate Chance
13. A Dash for Arabia
14. The Painted Safe
15. The Dagger Duel
16. The Double Disguise
17. The Death Weight
18. The Subterfuge
19. The Cryptic Maze
20. The End of the Trail

THE HOUSE OF HATE, March 3, 1918–July 20, 1918

Director: George B. Seitz

Scenario: Bertram Millhauser from a story by Arthur B. Reeve and Charles
A. Logne

Cast: Antonio Moreno, Paul Clerget, Peggy Shanor, John Webb, Paul
Dillon, John Gilmour, Floyd Buckley, Joe Cuny

Chapter Titles:

1. The Hooded Terror
2. The Tiger's Eye
3. A Woman's Perfidy
4. The Man from Java
5. Spies Within
6. A Living Target
7. The Germ Menace
8. The Untold Secret
9. Poisoned Darts
10. Double Crossed
11. Haunts of Evil
12. Flashes in the Dark
13. Enemy Aliens
14. Underworld Allies
15. The False Signal
16. The Vial of Death
17. The Death Switch

   18. At the Pistol's Point
   19. The Hooded Terror Unmasked
   20. Following Old Glory

THE LIGHTNING RAIDER, January 5, 1919–April 13, 1919
Director: George B. Seitz
Scenario: George B. Seitz and Bertram Millhauser
Cast: Warner Oland, Harry Gsell, Ruby Hoffman, William Burt
Chapter Titles:
   1. The Ebony Block
   2. The Counterplot
   3. Underworld Terrors
   4. Through Doors of Steel
   5. The Brass Key
   6. The Mystic Box
   7. Meshes of Evil
   8. Cave of Dread
   9. Falsely Accused
  10. The Baited Trap
  11. The Bars of Death
  12. Hurled into Space
  13. The White Roses
  14. Cleared of Guilt
  15. Wu Fang Atones

THE BLACK SECRET, November 9, 1919–February 15, 1920
Director: George B. Seitz
Scenario: Bertram Millhauser from the novel *In Secret* by Robert W.
    Chambers
Cast: Walter McGrail, Wallace McCutcheon, George B. Seitz, Harry
    Gsell
Chapter Titles:
   1. The Great Secret
   2. Marked for Death
   3. The Gas Chamber
   4. Below the Water Line
   5. The Acid Bath
   6. The Unknown
   7. The Betrayal
   8. A Crippled Hand
   9. Webbs of Deceit
  10. The Inn of Dread
  11. The Death Studio
  12. The Chance Trail
  13. Wings of Mystery
  14. The Hidden Way
  15. The Secret Host

FOX FILM COMPANY

850 10th Avenue
New York, N.Y.

THE WHITE MOLL, July 24, 1920
Director: Harry Millarde
Cast: Richard C. Travers, J. Thornton Baston, Eva Gordon, William
Harvey, Walter Lewis, Blanch Davenport, Charles Slatter, John
Woodford, George Pauncefort, John P. Wade

THE TIGER'S CLUB, October 16, 1920
Director: Charles Giblyn
Cast: Thomas Carrigan, J. Thornton Baston, John Davidson, Frank Evans,
John Woodford, Ruby Hoffman, Albert Tavernier

THE THIEF, December 11, 1920
Director: Charles Giblyn
Cast: Charles Waldron, Wallace McCutcheon, George Howard, Sidney
Herbert, Dorothy Cummings, Anthony Merlo

THE MOUNTAIN WOMAN, February 5, 1921
Director: Charles Giblyn
Cast: Corliss Giles, Richard C. Travers, George Barnum, John Dillon,
Warner Richmond, J. Thornton Baston, Charles Graham

KNOW YOUR MEN, April 2, 1921
Director: Charles Giblyn
Cast: Wilfred Lytell, C. Downing Clarke, Harry C. Browne, Estar Banks,
Byron Douglas, William Eville

BEYOND PRICE, May 21, 1921
Director: J. Searle Dawley
Cast: Vernon Steele, Nora Reed, Arthur Gordoni, Louis Haines, Maude
Turner Gordon, Byron Douglas, Ottola Nesmith, Dorothy Walters,
Dorothy Allen, J. Thornton Baston, Charles Sutton

A VIRGIN PARADISE, August 20, 1921
Director: J. Searle Dawley
Cast: Robert Elliott, J. Thornton Baston, Alan Edwards, Lynn Pratt,
Henrietta Floyd, Grace Beaumont, Mary Beth Barnelle, Lewis Seeley,
Charles Sutton, Hal Clarendon

ANY WIFE, February 18, 1922
Director: Herbert Brenon
Cast: Holmes Herbert, Gilbert Emery, Lawrence Johnson, Augustus Bal-
four, Eulalie Jensen

THE BROADWAY PEACOCK, February 25, 1922
Director: Charles J. Brabin
Cast: Joseph Stryker, Doris Raton

WITHOUT FEAR, April 29, 1922
Director: Kenneth Webb
Cast: Robert Elliot, Charles MacKay, Marie Burke, Robert Agnew, Macey Harlam

PATHÉ FILM COMPANY

25 W. 45th Street
New York, N.Y.

PLUNDER, January 28, 1923
Director: George B. Seitz
Scenario: George B. Seitz and Bertram Millhauser
Cast: Warren Krech (William), Harry Semels, Wally Oettel, Tom McIntyre, Elwood J. Pool
Chapter Titles:
1. The Bandaged Man
2. Held by the Enemy
3. The Hidden Thing
4. Ruin
5. To Beat a Knave
6. Heights of Hazard
7. Mocked From the Grave
8. The Human Target
9. Game Clear Through
10. Against Time
11. Spunk
12. Under the Floor
13. The Swamp of Lost Souls
14. The Madman
15. A King's Ransom

EPINAY FILM COMPANY

Paris, France

TERROR, June 25, 1924
Director: Edward Jose
Cast: Robert Lee, Arlette Marchal, Henry Baudin, Martin Mitchell, Paul Vermoyal
Released in the United States under the title: "The Perils of Paris"